Department of Health

Care Homes for Older People

National Minimum Standards

and

The Care Homes Regulations 2001

London: TSO

Published by TSO (The Stationery Office) and available from:

Online
www.tso.co.uk/bookshop

Mail, Telephone, Fax & E-mail
TSO
PO Box 29, Norwich, NR3 1GN
Telephone orders/General enquiries: 0870 600 5522
Fax orders: 0870 600 5533
E-mail: book.orders@tso.co.uk
Textphone 0870 240 3701

TSO Shops
123 Kingsway, London, WC2B 6PQ
020 7242 6393 Fax 020 7242 6394
68-69 Bull Street, Birmingham B4 6AD
0121 236 9696 Fax 0121 236 9699
9-21 Princess Street, Manchester M60 8AS
0161 834 7201 Fax 0161 833 0634
16 Arthur Street, Belfast BT1 4GD
028 9023 8451 Fax 028 9023 5401
18-19 High Street, Cardiff CF10 1PT
029 2039 5548 Fax 029 2038 4347
71 Lothian Road, Edinburgh EH3 9AZ
0870 606 5566 Fax 0870 606 5588

TSO Accredited Agents
(see Yellow Pages)

and through good booksellers

Published with the permission of the Department of Health
on behalf of the Controller of Her Majesty's Stationery Office.

First published 2002
Second edition 2003
Second impression 2003

ISBN 0 11 322607 1

Web Access

This document is available on the DoH internet website at:
http://www.doh.gov.uk/ncsc

Printed in the United Kingdom for the Stationery Office
160297   C60   12/03

National Minimum Standards for Care Homes for Older People

A statement of national minimum standards published by the Secretary of State for Health under section 23(1) of the Care Standards Act 2000.

February 2003

National Minimum Standards for Care Homes for Older People

Note

This document contains a statement of national minimum standards published by the Secretary of State under section 23(1) of the Care Standards Act 2000. The statement is applicable to care homes (as defined by section 3 of that Act) which provide accommodation, together with nursing or personal care, for older people.

The statement is accompanied, for explanatory purposes only, by an introduction to the statement as a whole, and a further introduction to each group of standards.

Each individual standard is numbered and consists of the numbered heading and numbered paragraphs. Each standard is, for explanatory purposes only, preceded by a title and an indication of the intended outcome in relation to that standard.

Department of Health

Contents

Introduction

Aims

This document sets out National Minimum Standards for Care Homes for Older People, which form the basis on which the new National Care Standards Commission will determine whether such care homes meet the needs, and secure the welfare and social inclusion, of the people who live there.

The national minimum standards set out in this document are core standards which apply to all care homes providing accommodation and nursing or personal care for older people. The standards apply to homes for which registration as care homes is required.

While broad in scope, these standards acknowledge the unique and complex needs of individuals, and the additional specific knowledge, skills and facilities needed in order for a care home to deliver an individually tailored and comprehensive service. Certain of the standards do not apply to pre-existing homes including local authority homes, "Royal Charter" homes and other homes not previously required to register. The standards do not apply to independent hospitals, hospices, clinics or establishments registered to take patients detained under the Mental Health Act 1983.

Regulatory Context

These standards are published by the Secretary of State for Health in accordance with section 23 of the Care Standards Act 2000 (CSA). They will apply from 1 June 2003, unless otherwise stated in any standard.

The Care Standards Act created the National Care Standards Commission (NCSC), an independent non-governmental public body, which regulates social and health care services previously regulated by local councils and health authorities. In addition, it extended the scope of regulation significantly to other services not previously registered, including domiciliary care agencies, fostering agencies and residential family centres.

The CSA sets out a broad range of regulation making powers covering, amongst other matters, the management, staff, premises and conduct of social and independent healthcare establishments and agencies.

Under the Care Standards Act the Secretary of State for Health has powers to publish statements of National Minimum Standards. In assessing whether a care home conforms to the Care Homes Regulations 2001, which **are** mandatory, the National Care Standards Commission **must** take the standards into account. However, the Commission **may** also take into account any other factors it considers reasonable or relevant to do so.

Compliance with national minimum standards is not itself enforceable, but compliance with regulations is enforceable subject to national standards being taken into account.

The Commission may conclude that a care home has been in breach of the regulations even though the home largely meets the standards. The Commission also has discretion to conclude that the regulations have been complied with by means other than those set out in the national minimum standards.

Structure and Approach

The National Minimum Standards for Care Homes for Older People focus on achievable outcomes for service users - that is, the impact on the individual of the facilities and services of the home. The standards are grouped under the following key topics, which highlight aspects of individuals' lives identified during the stakeholder consultation as most important to service users:

- Choice of home

- Health and personal care

- Daily life and social activities

- Complaints and protection

- Environment

- Staffing

- Management and administration

Each topic is prefaced by a statement of good practice, which sets out the rationale for the standards that follow. The standards themselves are numbered and the full set of numbered paragraphs needs to be met in order to achieve compliance with the standard. Each standard is preceded by a statement of the intended outcome for service users to be achieved by the care home.

While the standards are qualitative – they provide a tool for judging the quality of life of service users – they are also measurable. Regulators will look for evidence that the standards are being met and a good quality of life enjoyed by service users through:

- discussions with service users, families and friends, staff and managers and others;

- observation of daily life in the home;

- scrutiny of written policies, procedures and records.

The involvement of lay assessors in inspections will help ensure a focus on outcomes for, and quality of life of, service users.

The following cross-cutting themes underpin the drafting of the National Minimum Standards for Care Homes for Older People:

- **Focus on service users.** Modernising Social Services (1998) called for standards that "focus on the key areas that most affect the quality of life experienced by service users, as well as physical standards" [4.48]. The consultation process for developing the standards, and recent research, confirm the importance of this emphasis on results for service users. In applying the standards, regulators will look for evidence that the facilities, resources, policies, activities and services of the home lead to positive outcomes for, and the active participation of, service users.

- **Fitness for purpose.** The regulatory powers provided by the CSA are designed to ensure that care home managers, staff and premises are 'fit for their purpose'. In applying the standards, regulators will look for evidence that a home – whether providing a long-term placement, short-term rehabilitation, nursing care or specialist service - is successful in achieving its stated aims and objectives.

- **Comprehensiveness.** Life in a care home is made up of a range of services and facilities which may be of greater or lesser importance to different service users. In applying the standards, regulators will consider how the total service package offered by the care home contributes to the overall personal and health care needs and preferences of service users, and how the home works with other services / professionals to ensure the individual's inclusion in the community.

- **Meeting assessed needs.** In applying the standards, inspectors will look for evidence that care homes meet assessed needs of service users and that individuals' changing needs continue to be met. The assessment and service user plan carried out in the care home should be based on the care management individual care plan and determination of registered nursing input (where relevant) produced by local social services and NHS staff where they are purchasing the service. The needs of privately funded service users should be assessed by the care home prior to offering a place.

- **Quality services.** The Government's modernising agenda, including the new regulatory framework, aims to ensure greater assurance of quality services rather than having to live with second best. In applying the standards, regulators will seek evidence of a commitment to continuous improvement, quality services, support, accommodation and facilities which assure a good quality of life and health for service users.

- **Quality workforce.** Competent, well-trained managers and staff are fundamental to achieving good quality care for service users. The National Training Organisation for social care, TOPSS, is developing national occupational standards for care staff, including induction competencies and foundation programmes. In applying the standards, regulators will look for evidence that registered managers and staff achieve TOPSS requirements and comply with any code of practice published by the General Social Care Council.

Context and Purpose

These standards, and the regulatory framework within which they operate, should be viewed in the context of the Government's overall policy objectives for older people. These objectives emphasise the need to maintain and promote independence wherever possible, through rehabilitation and community support. A variety of specialist provision will be required to help achieve these objectives. Good quality care homes have an important part to play in that provision.

These standards have been prepared in response to extensive consultation and aim to be realistic, proportionate, fair and transparent. They provide minimum standards below which no provider is expected to operate, and are designed to ensure the protection of service users and safeguard and promote their health, welfare and quality of life.

1

Choice of Home

INTRODUCTION TO STANDARDS 1 TO 6

Each home must produce a statement of purpose and other information materials (service users' guide) setting out its aims and objectives, the range of facilities and services it offers to residents and the terms and conditions on which it does so in its contract of occupancy with residents. In this way prospective residents can make a fully informed choice about whether or not the home is suitable and able to meet the individual's particular needs. Copies of the most recent inspection reports should also be made available. The statement of purpose will enable inspectors to assess how far the home's claims to be able to meet resident's requirements and expectations are being fulfilled. While it would be unreasonable and unnecessary to expect every home to offer the same range of facilities and lifestyle, older people do want a range of choice when they decide to move into a care home. By requiring proprietors to 'set out their stall', the problem of leaving choice to chance is overcome. There can be no room for doubt either on the part of the prospective resident, the inspector or the proprietor. In this way diversity and range of choice across the care home sector can be maintained. For example:

- if the home says it provides for the needs of people with dementia, it will have to make clear in the prospectus how this is done - for example, small group living and structured activities, with décor and signage helpful to people with dementia;

- if a home says it can cater for the needs of Muslim elders whose first language is not English, it must show that it can do so by, amongst other things, showing that it can prepare and provide halal food, offer links with the local mosque and provide appropriate washing facilities and demonstrate that it employs staff who speak appropriate languages;

- a home will make clear in its information materials whether it aims to offer residents a family-like environment at one end of the spectrum, or whether it offers hotel-style accommodation where residents live more independently from one another at the other.

The key must be the choice and the opportunity to exercise choice. This can only be achieved if full information is provided.

See: *Choosing a Care Home*, OFT (1998).

Information

OUTCOME

Prospective service users have the information they need to make an informed choice about where to live.

STANDARD 1

1.1 **The registered person produces and makes available to service users an up-to-date statement of purpose setting out the aims, objectives, philosophy of care, services and facilities, and terms and conditions of the home; and provides a service users' guide to the home for current and prospective residents. The statement of purpose clearly sets out the physical environment standards met by a home in relation to standards 20.1, 20.4, 21.3, 21.4, 22.2, 22.5, 23.3 and 23.10: a summary of this information appears in the home's service user's guide.**

1.2 The service user's guide is written in plain English and made available in a language and/or format suitable for intended residents and includes:

- a brief description of the services provided;
- A description of the individual accommodation and communal space provided;
- relevant qualifications and experience of the registered provider, manager and staff;
- the number of places provided and any special needs or interests catered for;
- a copy of the most recent inspection report;
- a copy of the complaints procedure;
- service users' views of the home.

1.3 Service users and their representatives are given information in writing in a relevant language and format about how to contact the local office of the National Care Standards Commission and local social services and health care authorities.

Contract

OUTCOME

Each service user has a written contract/statement of terms and conditions with the home

STANDARD 2

2.1 **Each service user is provided with a statement of terms and conditions at the point of moving into the home (or contract if purchasing their care privately).**

2.2   The statement of terms and conditions includes:

- rooms to be occupied;

- overall care and services (including food) covered by fee;

- fees payable and by whom (service user, local or health authority, relative or another);

- additional services (including food and equipment) to be paid for over and above those included in the fees;

- rights and obligations of the service user and registered provider and who is liable if there is a breach of contract;

- terms and conditions of occupancy, including period of notice (eg short/long term intermediate care/respite).

Needs Assessment

OUTCOME

No service user moves into the home without having had his/her needs assessed and been assured that these will be met.

STANDARD 3

3.1   New service users are admitted only on the basis of a full assessment undertaken by people trained to do so, and to which the prospective service user, his/her representatives (if any) and relevant professionals have been party.

3.2   For individuals referred through Care Management arrangements, the registered person obtains a summary of the Care Management (health and social services) assessment and a copy of the Care Plan produced for care management purposes.

3.3   For individuals who are self-funding and without a Care Management assessment/ Care Plan, the registered person carries out a needs assessment covering:

- personal care and physical well-being;

- diet and weight, including dietary preferences;

- sight, hearing and communication;

- oral health;

- foot care;

- mobility and dexterity;

- history of falls;

- continence;

- medication usage;

- mental state and cognition;

- social interests, hobbies, religious and cultural needs;

- personal safety and risk;
- carer and family involvement and other social contacts/relationships.

3.4 Each service user has a plan of care for daily living, and longer term outcomes, based on the Care Management assessment and Care Plan or on the home's own needs assessment (see Standard 7, Service User Plan).

3.5 The registered nursing input required by service users in homes providing nursing care is determined by NHS registered nurses using a recognised assessment tool, according to Department of Health guidance.

Meeting Needs

OUTCOME

Service users and their representatives know that the home they enter will meet their needs.

STANDARD 4

4.1 The registered person is able to demonstrate the home's capacity to meet the assessed needs (including specialist needs) of individuals admitted to the home.

4.2 All specialised services offered (eg services for people with dementia or other cognitive impairments, sensory impairment, physical disabilities, learning disabilities, intermediate or respite care) are demonstrably based on current good practice, and reflect relevant specialist and clinical guidance.

4.3 The needs and preference of specific minority ethnic communities, social/cultural or religious groups catered for are understood and met.

4.4 Staff individually and collectively have the skills and experience to deliver the services and care which the home offers to provide.

Trial Visits

OUTCOME

Prospective service users and their relatives and friends have an opportunity to visit and assess the quality, facilities and suitability of the home.

STANDARD 5

5.1 The registered person ensures that prospective service users are invited to visit the home and to move in on a trial basis, before they and/or their representatives make a decision to stay; unplanned admissions are avoided where possible.

5.2 Prospective service users are given the opportunity for staff to meet them in their own homes or current situation if different.

5.3 When an emergency admission is made, the registered person undertakes to inform the service user within 48 hours about key aspects, rules and routines of the service, and to meet all other admission criteria set out in Standards 2 – 4 within five working days.

Intermediate Care

OUTCOME

Service users assessed and referred solely for intermediate care are helped to maximise their independence and return home.

STANDARD 6

6.1 Where service users are admitted only for intermediate care, dedicated accommodation is provided, together with specialised facilities, equipment and staff, to deliver short term intensive rehabilitation and enable service users to return home.

6.2 Rehabilitation facilities are sited in dedicated space and include equipment for therapies and treatment, as well as equipment to promote activities of daily living and mobility.

6.3 Staff are qualified and/or are trained and appropriately supervised to use techniques for rehabilitation including treatment and recovery programmes, promotion of mobility, continence and self-care, and outreach programmes to re-establish community living.

6.4 Staff are deployed, and specialist services from relevant professions including occupational and physiotherapists are provided or secured in sufficient numbers and with sufficient competence and skills, to meet the assessed needs of service users admitted for rehabilitation.

6.5 The service user placed for intermediate care is not admitted for long term care unless and until the requirements regarding information, assessment and care planning (Standards 1, 3 and 7) are met.

2

Health and Personal Care

INTRODUCTION TO STANDARDS 7 TO 11

The health and personal care which a resident receives will be based on the individual's needs. It is, therefore, impossible to lay down standards to cover precisely every aspect of care required for all residents. Because of this, the assessment process and the care plan for the individual are seen as crucial in standard setting. What is found during the assessment process should be put into the service user's plan. The plan is the end point of the assessment of the individual. Care must then be delivered in accordance with the service user's plan for that individual. Thus the plan becomes the yardstick for judging whether appropriate care is delivered to the individual resident. It is a dynamic document, which will change as regular assessment of the resident reveals changing needs.

Often the initial assessment, which determines whether or not an individual goes into a care home, will be made by people outside the home. In laying down what the assessment should be based on, the national minimum standards do not seek to hold proprietors/managers to account for the actions of others. However, a resident should not go into a home without a full assessment having been made, except in the case of an emergency. The proprietor/manager and relevant professional staff within the home should be party to that full assessment and only accept a new resident if they feel the home can adequately meet the needs of the prospective resident as determined through that assessment.

Guidelines published by the Royal Pharmaceutical Society (1991), Age Concern (Levenson 1998), Royal College of Physicians (1997), the Royal College of Nursing (1996, 1997) and the Nursing and Midwifery Council (1992) are referred to or drawn on in the following section and should be adhered to.

Privacy and Dignity

The principles on which the home's philosophy of care is based must be ones which ensure that residents are treated with respect, that their dignity is preserved at all times, and that their right to privacy is always observed. Fundamentally, the test of whether these principles are put into practice or not will be a matter for the individual resident's own judgement:

- how am I treated by staff when they are bathing me and helping me dress?
- how do they speak to me?

- am I consulted in matters to do with my own care and matters that concern residents as a whole?
- are my wishes respected?
- are my views taken into account?
- do staff regard me as a real person with desires, hopes and expectations just like them?

However, not all residents will be able to make that judgement and communicate it to their relatives or representatives, the staff or inspectors. Other tests will have to be used which reflect the principles which must underpin all that goes on in the home. This section sets out a number of key standards which will enable managers and inspectors to judge the home's performance in relation to its governing philosophy. Guidelines published over the past 20 years have emphasised the importance of valuing privacy, dignity, choice, rights, independence and fulfilment. These values underpin the national minimum standards.

See: Good practice guides such as *Home Life; Homes are for Living In; A Better Home Life; Creating a Home from Home.*

Dying and Death

The process of dying and death itself must never be regarded as routine by managers and staff. The quality of the care which residents receive in their last days is as important as the quality of life which they experience prior to this. This means that their physical and emotional needs must be met, their comfort and well-being attended to and their wishes respected. Pain and distress should be controlled and privacy and dignity at all times preserved. The professional skills of palliative care staff can help homes ensure the comfort of residents who are dying. There are a number of specialist agencies providing practical assistance and advice, such as Marie Curie and Macmillan nurses, which can be called upon.

The impact of the death of a resident on the community of residents may be significant and it is important that the home ensures that opportunities are available for residents to come to terms with it in ways which the individual residents find comforting and acceptable. Thus opportunities for meditation and reflection and for contact with local and religious and spiritual leaders should be provided.

Residents should be encouraged to express their wishes about what they want to happen when death approaches and to provide instructions about the formalities to be observed after they have died. Cultural and religious preferences must be observed.

There should also be an openness and willingness on the part of staff to talk about dying and death and about those residents who have recently died. Staff themselves, especially young and inexperienced staff, may also need support at such times. The needs of family and friends should also be attended to. Because each individual will have their own preferences and expectations, it is impossible to lay down standards for observances and practices which can apply in every circumstance. However it is essential for homes to have clear policies and procedures about how they ensure that residents' last days are spent in comfort and dignity and that their wishes are observed throughout.

See: Counsel and Care (1995); National Council for Hospice and Specialist Palliative Care Services (1997).

Service User Plan

OUTCOME

The service user's health, personal and social care needs are set out in an individual plan of care.

STANDARD 7

7.1 **A service user plan of care generated from a comprehensive assessment (see Standard 3) is drawn up with each service user and provides the basis for the care to be delivered.**

7.2 The service user's plan sets out in detail the action which needs to be taken by care staff to ensure that all aspects of the health, personal and social care needs of the service user (see Standard 3) are met.

7.3 The service user's plan meets relevant clinical guidelines produced by the relevant professional bodies concerned with the care of older people, and includes a risk assessment, with particular attention to prevention of falls.

7.4 The service user's plan is reviewed by care staff in the home at least once a month, updated to reflect changing needs and current objectives for health and personal care, and actioned.

7.5 Where the service user is on the Care Programme Approach or subject to requirements under the Mental Health Act 1983, the service user's plan takes this fully into account.

7.6 The plan is drawn up with the involvement of the service user, recorded in a style accessible to the service user; agreed and signed by the service user whenever capable and/or representative (if any).

Health Care

OUTCOME

Service users make decisions about their lives with assistance as needed.

STANDARD 8

8.1   The registered person promotes and maintains service users' health and ensures access to health care services to meet assessed needs.

8.2   Care staff maintain the personal and oral hygiene of each service user and, wherever possible, support the service user's own capacity for self-care.

8.3   Service users are assessed, by a person trained to do so, to identify those service users who have developed, or are at risk of developing, pressure sores and appropriate intervention is recorded in the plan of care.

8.4   The incidence of pressure sores, their treatment and outcome, are recorded in the service user's individual plan of care and reviewed on a continuing basis.

8.5   Equipment necessary for the promotion of tissue viability and prevention or treatment of pressure sores is provided.

8.6   The registered person ensures that professional advice about the promotion of continence is sought and acted upon and aids and equipment needed are provided.

8.7   The service user's psychological health is monitored regularly and preventive and restorative care provided.

8.8   Opportunities are given for appropriate exercise and physical activity; appropriate interventions are carried out for service users identified as at risk of falling.

8.9   Nutritional screening is undertaken on admission and subsequently on a periodic basis, a record maintained of nutrition, including weight gain or loss, and appropriate action taken.

8.10   The registered person enables service users to register with a GP of their choice (if the GP is in agreement).

8.11   The registered person enables service users to have access to specialist medical, nursing, dental, pharmaceutical, chiropody and therapeutic services and care from hospitals and community health services according to need.

8.12   Service users have access to hearing and sight tests and appropriate aids, according to need.

8.13   The registered person ensures that service users' entitlements to NHS services are upheld in accordance with guidance and legislation, including the standards in the National Service Framework, by providing information about entitlements and ensuring access to advice.

Medication

OUTCOME

Service users, where appropriate, are responsible for their own medication, and are protected by the home's policies and procedures for dealing with medicines.

STANDARD 9

9.1 **The registered person ensures that there is a policy and staff adhere to procedures, for the receipt, recording, storage, handling, administration and disposal of medicines, and service users are able to take responsibility for their own medication if they wish, within a risk management framework.**

9.2 The service user, following assessment as able to self-administer medication, has a lockable space in which to store medication, to which suitably trained, designated care staff may have access with the service user's permission.

9.3 Records are kept of all medicines received, administered and leaving the home or disposed of to ensure that there is no mishandling. A record is maintained of current medication for each service user (including those self-administering).

9.4 Medicines in the custody of the home are handled according to the requirements of the Medicines Act 1968, guidelines from the Royal Pharmaceutical Society, the requirements of the Misuse of Drugs Act 1971 and nursing staff abide by the UKCC Standards for the administration of medicines.

9.5 Controlled Drugs administered by staff are stored in a metal cupboard, which complies with the Misuse of Drugs (Safe Custody) Regulations 1973.

9.6 Medicines, including Controlled Drugs, for service users receiving nursing care, are administered by a medical practitioner or registered nurse.

9.7 In residential care homes, all medicines, including Controlled Drugs, (except those for self-administration) are administered by designated and appropriately trained staff. The administration of Controlled Drugs is witnessed by another designated, appropriately trained member of staff.

The training for care staff must be accredited and must include:

- basic knowledge of how medicines are used and how to recognise and deal with problems in use;

- the principles behind all aspects of the home's policy on medicines handling and records.

9.8 Receipt, administration and disposal of Controlled Drugs are recorded in a Controlled Drugs register.

9.9 The registered manager seeks information and advice from a pharmacist regarding medicines policies within the home and medicines dispensed for individuals in the home.

9.10 Staff monitor the condition of the service user on medication and call in the GP if staff are concerned about any change in condition that may be a result of medication, and prompt the review of medication on a regular basis.

9.11 When a service user dies, medicines should be retained for a period of seven days in case there is a coroner's inquest.

Privacy and Dignity

OUTCOME

Service users feel they are treated with respect and their right to privacy is upheld.

STANDARD 10

10.1 **The arrangements for health and personal care ensure that service user's privacy and dignity are respected at all times, and with particular regard to:**

- personal care-giving, including nursing, bathing, washing, using the toilet or commode;
- consultation with, and examination by, health and social care professionals;
- consultation with legal and financial advisors;
- maintaining social contacts with relatives and friends;
- entering bedrooms, toilets and bathrooms;
- following death.

10.2 Service users have easy access to a telephone for use in private and receive their mail unopened.

10.3 Service users wear their own clothes at all times.

10.4 All staff use the term of address preferred by the service user.

10.5 All staff are instructed during induction on how to treat service users with respect at all times.

10.6 Medical examination and treatment are provided in the service user's own room.

10.7 Where service users have chosen to share a room, screening is provided to ensure that their privacy is not compromised when personal care is being given or at any other time.

Dying and Death

OUTCOME

Service users are assured that at the time of their death, staff will treat them and their family with care, sensitivity and respect.

STANDARD 11

11.1 **Care and comfort are given to service users who are dying, their death is handled with dignity and propriety, and their spiritual needs, rites and functions observed.**

11.2   Care staff make every effort to ensure that the service user receives appropriate attention and pain relief.

11.3   The service user's wishes concerning terminal care and arrangements after death are discussed and carried out.

11.4   The service user's family and friends are involved (if that is what the service user wants) in planning for and dealing with increasing infirmity, terminal illness and death.

11.5   The privacy and dignity of the service user who is dying are maintained at all times.

11.6   Service users are able to spend their final days in their own rooms, surrounded by their personal belongings, unless there are strong medical reasons to prevent this.

11.7   The registered person ensures that staff and service users who wish to offer comfort to a service user who is dying are enabled and supported to do so.

11.8   Palliative care, practical assistance and advice, and bereavement counselling are provided by trained professionals /specialist agencies if the service user wishes.

11.9   The changing needs of service users with deteriorating conditions or dementia – for personal support or technical aids – are reviewed and met swiftly to ensure the individual retains maximum control.

11.10   Relatives and friends of a service user who is dying are able to stay with him/her, unless the service user makes it clear that he or she does not want them to, for as long as they wish.

11.11   The body of a service user who has died is handled with dignity, and time is allowed for family and friends to pay their respects.

11.12   Policies and procedures for handling dying and death are in place and observed by staff.

3

Daily Life and Social Activities

INTRODUCTION TO STANDARDS 12 TO 15

The fact that individuals have reached a later stage of life does not mean that their social, cultural, recreational and occupational characteristics, which have taken a lifetime to emerge, suddenly disappear. Older people moving into homes will have differing expectations and preferences as to lifestyle within the residential setting. The degree to which, and the way in which, social life is organised within the home, along with the range of activities available, must be set out in the home's information materials (statement of purpose and service user's guide) so that prospective residents get a clear idea of what is on offer. Some people will want an active, well-organised social life; in contrast, others will want a level of privacy and independence from other residents, although looking to the home for resources such as a library, quiet room or a space for religious observance. The capacity for social activity will vary according to the individual and many residents will need special support and assistance in engaging in the activities of daily life. For them, a structured daily life may well be a therapeutic requirement. Other people will search for a home which accommodates people with similar cultural, religious, professional or recreational interests. The standards have to take this wide variation in preferences and capacity into account. The information in the statement of purpose and service user's guide will be crucial in assessing whether a home is providing what it claims it sets out to provide.

Meals and Mealtimes

Residents regard the food they are given as one of the most important factors in determining their quality of life. It is important in maintaining their health and wellbeing. Failure to eat – through physical inability, depression, or because the food is inadequate or unappetising – can lead to malnutrition with serious consequences for health. Care staff should monitor the individual resident's food intake in as discreet and unregimented a way as possible. Care and tact should always be used. The availability, quality and style of presentation of food, along with the way in which staff assist residents at mealtimes, are crucial in ensuring residents receive a wholesome, appealing and nutritious diet. The social aspects of food - its preparation, presentation and consumption – are likely to have played a significant part in most people's lives, and it is important that homes make every effort to ensure this remains so for individuals once they move into care. While it is recognised that many residents will no longer be able to play an active part in preparing food – even snacks and light refreshment – many still want to retain some capacity to do so. In these situations, restriction on access to main kitchens because of health and safety considerations may present problems. It is important that homes look at alternative ways of maintaining residents' involvement - for example, by providing kitchenettes, organising cooking as part of a range of daily activities – and enabling residents to be involved in laying up and clearing the dining rooms if they wish to, before and after mealtimes. Individuals' food preferences, both personal and cultural/religious, are part of their individual identity and must always be observed. These should be ascertained at the point where an individual is considering moving into the home and the home must make it clear whether or not those preferences can be observed. Homes must not make false claims that they can properly provide kosher, halal, vegetarian and other diets if they cannot observe all the requirements associated with those diets in terms of purchase, storage, preparation and cooking of the food.

See: examples on: *Dementia* – Benson, S (1998), Clarke et al (1996), Marshall, M (1997);

Spiritual needs – Jewell, A (1998), Regan *et al* (1997);

Ethnicity – Jones *et al* (1992);

Learning disabilities – Ward, C (1998);

Food – Caroline Walker Trust (1995).

Social Contact and Activities

OUTCOME

Service users find the lifestyle experienced in the home matches their expectations and preferences, and satisfies their social, cultural, religious and recreational interests and needs.

STANDARD 12

12.1 **The routines of daily living and activities made available are flexible and varied to suit service users' expectations, preferences and capacities.**

12.2 Service users have the opportunity to exercise their choice in relation to:

- leisure and social activities and cultural interests;
- food, meals and mealtimes;
- routines of daily living;
- personal and social relationships;
- religious observance.

12.3 Service users' interests are recorded and they are given opportunities for stimulation through leisure and recreational activities in and outside the home which suit their needs, preferences and capacities; particular consideration is given to people with dementia and other cognitive impairments, those with visual, hearing or dual sensory impairments, those with physical disabilities or learning disabilities.

12.4 Up to date information about activities is circulated to all service users in formats suited to their capacities.

Community Contact

OUTCOME

Service users maintain contact with family/friends /representatives and the local community as they wish.

STANDARD 13

13.1 Service users are able to have visitors at any reasonable time and links with the local community are developed and/or maintained in accordance with service users' preferences.

13.2 Service users are able to receive visitors in private.

13.3 Service users are able to choose whom they see and do not see.

13.4 The registered person does not impose restrictions on visits except when requested to do so by service users, whose wishes are recorded.

13.5 Relatives, friends and representatives of service users are given written information about the home's policy on maintaining relatives and friends' involvement with service users at the time of moving into the home.

13.6 Involvement in the home by local community groups and/or volunteers accords with service users' preferences.

Autonomy and Choice

OUTCOME

Service users are helped to exercise choice and control over their lives.

STANDARD 14

14.1 The registered person conducts the home so as to maximise service users' capacity to exercise personal autonomy and choice.

14.2   Service users handle their own financial affairs for as long as they wish to and as long as they are able to and have the capacity to do so.

14.3   Service users and their relatives and friends are informed of how to contact external agents (e.g. advocates), who will act in their interests.

14.4   Service users are entitled to bring personal possessions with them, the extent of which will be agreed prior to admission.

14.5   Access to personal records, in accordance with the Data Protection Act 1998, is facilitated for service users.

Meals and Mealtimes

OUTCOME

Service users receive a wholesome appealing balanced diet in pleasing surroundings at times convenient to them.

STANDARD 15

15.1   The registered person ensures that service users receive a varied, appealing, wholesome and nutritious diet, which is suited to individual assessed and recorded requirements, and that meals are taken in a congenial setting and at flexible times.

15.2   Each service user is offered three full meals each day (at least one of which must be cooked) at intervals of not more than five hours.

15.3   Hot and cold drinks and snacks are available at all times and offered regularly. A snack meal should be offered in the evening and the interval between this and breakfast the following morning should be no more than 12 hours.

15.4   Food, including liquified meals, is presented in a manner which is attractive and appealing in terms of texture, flavour, and appearance, in order to maintain appetite and nutrition.

15.5   Special therapeutic diets/feeds are provided when advised by health care and dietetic staff, including adequate provision of calcium and vitamin D.

15.6   Religious or cultural dietary needs are catered for as agreed at admission and recorded in the care plan and food for special occasions is available.

15.7   The registered person ensures that there is a menu (changed regularly), offering a choice of meals in written or other formats to suit the capacities of all service users, which is given, read or explained to service users.

15.8   The registered person ensures that mealtimes are unhurried with service users being given sufficient time to eat.

15.9   Staff are ready to offer assistance in eating where necessary, discreetly, sensitively and individually, while independent eating is encouraged for as long as possible.

4

Complaints and Protection

INTRODUCTION TO STANDARDS 16 TO 18

The following section addresses the matter of how residents and/or their relatives and representatives can make complaints about anything which goes on in the home, both in terms of the treatment and care given by staff or the facilities which are provided. It deals with complaints procedures within the home relating to matters between the resident and the proprietor or manager. Complainants may also make their complaints directly to the National Care Standards Commission.

Whilst it is recognised that having a robust and effective complaints procedure which residents feel able to use is essential, this should not mean that the opportunity to make constructive suggestions (rather than complaints) is regarded as less important. Making suggestions about how things might be improved may create co-operative relationships within the home and prevent situations where complaints need to be made from developing. However, it is important to remember that many older people do not like to complain – either because it is difficult for them or because they are afraid of being victimised. If a home is truly committed to the principles outlined in earlier sections of this document, an open culture within the home will develop which enables residents, supporters and staff to feel confident in making suggestions and for making complaints where it is appropriate without any fear of victimisation. The NCSC will look to the quality assurance process and service user survey (Standard 33) for evidence of an open culture.

Complaints

OUTCOME

Service users and their relatives and friends are confident that their complaints will be listened to, taken seriously and acted upon.

STANDARD 16

16.1 **The registered person ensures that there is a simple, clear and accessible complaints procedure which includes the stages and timescales for the process, and that complaints are dealt with promptly and effectively.**

16.2 The registered person ensures that the home has a complaints procedure which specifies how complaints may be made and who will deal with them, with an assurance that they will be responded to within a maximum of 28 days.

16.3 A record is kept of all complaints made and includes details of investigation and any action taken.

16.4 The registered person ensures that written information is provided to all service users for referring a complaint to the NCSC at any stage, should the complainant wish to do so.

Rights

OUTCOME

Service users' legal rights are protected.

STANDARD 17

17.1 Service users have their legal rights protected, are enabled to exercise their legal rights directly and participate in the civic process if they wish.

17.2 Where service users lack capacity, the registered person facilitates access to available advocacy services.

17.3 Service users' rights to participate in the political process are upheld, for example, by enabling them to vote in elections.

Protection

OUTCOME

Service users are protected from abuse.

STANDARD 18

18.1 The registered person ensures that service users are safeguarded from physical, financial or material, psychological or sexual abuse, neglect, discriminatory abuse or self-harm, inhuman or degrading treatment, through deliberate intent, negligence or ignorance, in accordance with written policies.

18.2 Robust procedures for responding to suspicion or evidence of abuse or neglect (including whistle blowing) ensure the safety and protection of service users, including passing on concerns to the NCSC in accordance with the Public Interest Disclosure Act 1998 and Department of Health (DH) guidance No Secrets.

18.3   All allegations and incidents of abuse are followed up promptly and action taken is recorded.

18.4   Staff who may be unsuitable to work with vulnerable adults are referred, in accordance with the Care Standards Act, for consideration for inclusion on the Protection of Vulnerable Adults register.

18.5   The policies and practices of the home ensure that physical and/or verbal aggression by service users is understood and dealt with appropriately, and that physical intervention is used only as a last resort and in accordance with DH guidance.

18.6   The home's policies and practices regarding service users' money and financial affairs ensure service users' access to their personal financial records, safe storage of money and valuables, consultation on finances in private, and advice on personal insurance; and preclude staff involvement in assisting in the making of or benefiting from service users' wills.

5

Environment

INTRODUCTION TO STANDARDS 19 TO 26

The links between the style of home, its philosophy of care and its size, design and layout are interwoven. A home which sets out to offer family-like care is unlikely to be successful if it operates in a large building with high numbers of resident places. It would need special design features - being divided into smaller units each with its own communal focus, for example, - to measure up to its claim to offer a domestic, family-scale environment. On the other hand, someone looking for a 'hotel'-style home, may prefer a large home with more individual facilities than could be offered by the small family-style home.

Where special needs are catered for, the design and layout of the physical environment are crucial. People with a high level of visual impairment will require particular design features to help them negotiate the environment, many of which may be advantageous to all older people, but will be essential to them. Older people with learning disabilities may have been used to living in small group homes and other small scale settings when they were younger (at least since the development of community care policies) and are likely to prefer a continuation of that style of living as they get older. People with dementia have particular needs for the layout of communal space and associated signage which aid their remaining capacity. Other older people, however, could find some of these features patronising.

The onus will be on proprietors to make clear which clientele their homes are aimed at and to make sure the physical environment matches their requirements. This section does not seek to set out detailed standards to meet the wide variety of needs exhibited by different client groups. Proprietors will have to meet the claims they make in their statement of purpose in respect of these. Nevertheless, although the physical character of homes will vary according to the needs of their residents, there are certain standards of provision common to all homes and which must be met.

See: *Centre for Accessible Environments/NHS Estates* (1998); Marshall, M, (1997); Peace *et al* (1982); Torrington, J (1996); Health & Safety Executive (1993).

Premises

OUTCOME

Service users live in a safe, well-maintained environment.

STANDARD 19

19.1 **The location and layout of the home is suitable for its stated purpose; it is accessible, safe and well-maintained; meets service users' individual and collective needs in a comfortable and homely way and has been designed with reference to relevant guidance.**

19.2 A programme of routine maintenance and renewal of the fabric and decoration of the premises is produced and implemented with records kept.

19.3 Grounds are kept tidy, safe, attractive and accessible to service users, and allow access to sunlight.

19.4 Where a timescale has been set for compliance with any standard relating to the physical environment of the home, a plan and programme for achieving compliance is produced and followed and records kept.

19.5 The building complies with the requirements of the local fire service and environmental health department.

19.6 The use of CCTV cameras is restricted to entrance areas for security purposes only and does not intrude on the daily life of service users.

Shared Facilities

OUTCOME

Service users have access to safe and comfortable indoor and outdoor communal facilities.

STANDARD 20

20.1 **In all newly built homes and first time registrations the home provides sitting, recreational and dining space (referred to collectively as communal space) apart from service users' private accommodation and excluding corridors and entrance hall amounting to at least 4.1sq metres for each service user.**

20.2 Communal space is available which includes:

- rooms in which a variety of social, cultural and religious activities can take place; and service users can meet visitors in private;
- dining room(s) to cater for all service users;

- a smoke-free sitting room.

20.3 There is outdoor space for service users, accessible to those in wheelchairs or with other mobility problems, with seating and designed to meet the needs of all service users including those with physical, sensory and cognitive impairments.

20.4 Pre-existing care homes, which provide at least 4.1sq metres of communal space for each service user as at 16 August 2002 continue to do so. Where they did not provide that amount of space as at that date, they provide at least the same communal space for each service user as they provided as at 31 March 2002.

20.5 Where intermediate care is provided, dedicated space is available for this service group.

20.6 Lighting in communal rooms is domestic in character, sufficiently bright and positioned to facilitate reading and other activities.

20.7 Furnishings of communal rooms are domestic in character and of good quality, and suitable for the range of interests and activities preferred by service users.

Lavatories and Washing Facilities

OUTCOME

Service users have sufficient and suitable lavatories and washing facilities.

STANDARD 21

21.1 Toilet, washing and bathing facilities are provided to meet the needs of service users.

21.2 There are accessible toilets for service users, clearly marked, close to lounge and dining areas.

21.3 In all newly-built homes, new extensions to homes and first time registrations there is a ratio of 1 assisted bath (or assisted shower provided this meets residents needs) to 8 service users. Where suitably adapted en-suite bathing/shower facilities are provided in service users' rooms, these rooms can be excluded from this calculation.

21.4 Pre-existing care homes, which provided at least 1 assisted bath (or assisted showers provided this meets residents needs) to 8 service users as at 16 August 2002 continue to do so. Where they did not provide that ratio of baths as at that date, they provide at least the same number of assisted baths for service users as they provided as at 31 March 2002.

21.5 Each service user has a toilet within close proximity of his/her private accommodation.

21.6   En-suite facilities (at minimum a toilet and hand-basin) are provided to all service users in all new build, extensions and all first time registrations from 1 April 2002.

21.7   The installation of en-suite facilities should be in addition to the minimum usable floor space standards in any service user's room.

21.8   En-suite facilities in rooms accommodating service users using wheelchairs or other aids, are accessible to them.

21.9   Any sluices provided are located separately from service users' wc and bathing facilities.

Adaptations and Equipment

OUTCOME

Service users have the specialist equipment they require to maximise their independence.

STANDARD 22

22.1   The registered person demonstrates that an assessment of the premises and facilities has been made by suitably qualified persons, including a qualified occupational therapist, with specialist knowledge of the client groups catered for, and provides evidence that the recommended disability equipment has been secured or provided and environmental adaptations made to meet the needs of service users.

22.2   Service users have access to all parts of service users' communal and private space, through the provision of ramps and passenger lifts, where required to achieve this, or stair/chair lifts where they meet the assessed needs of service users and the appropriate requirements of the Environmental Health departments and the Health and Safety Executive.

22.3   The home provides grab rails and other aids in corridors, bathrooms, toilets, communal rooms and where necessary in service users' own accommodation.

22.4   Aids, hoists and assisted toilets and baths are installed which are capable of meeting the assessed needs of service users.

22.5   Doorways into communal areas, service users' rooms, bathing and toilet facilities and other spaces to which wheelchair users have access, should be of width sufficient to allow wheelchair users adequate access. In all newly built homes, new extensions to homes and first time registrations doorways into areas to which wheelchair users have access should have a clear opening of 800mm.

22.6   Facilities, including communication aids (eg a loop system), and signs are provided to assist the needs of all service users, taking account of the needs, for example, of those with hearing impairment, visual impairment, dual sensory impairments, learning disabilities or dementia or other cognitive impairment, where necessary.

22.7   Storage areas are provided for aids and equipment, including wheelchairs.

22.8   Call systems with an accessible alarm facility are provided in every room.

Individual Accommodation: Space Requirements

OUTCOME
Service users' own rooms suit their needs.

STANDARD 23

23.1   The home provides accommodation for each service user which meets minimum space as follows:

23.2   In all new build, extensions and first time registrations, all places are provided in single rooms with a minimum of 12sq metres usable floor-space (excluding en-suite facilities).

23.3   Pre-existing care homes, with rooms which provided at least 10 sq metres of useable space for each service user as at 16 August 2002, continue to provide that amount of space in those rooms. Pre-existing care homes with rooms which did not provide that amount of space as at that date, provide at least the same useable floor space in those rooms as they provided as at 31 March 2002.

23.4   Single rooms accommodating wheelchair users have at least 12sq metres usable floor space (excluding en-suite facilities).

23.5   Room dimensions and layout options ensure that there is room on either side of the bed, to enable access for carers and any equipment needed.

23.6   Where rooms are shared, they are occupied by no more than two service users who have made a positive choice to share with each other.

23.7   When a shared place becomes vacant, the remaining service user has the opportunity to choose not to share, by moving into a different room if necessary.

23.8   Rooms which are currently shared have at least 16sq metres of usable floor space (excluding en-suite facilities).

23.9   In new build, extensions and all first time registrations, service users wishing to share accommodation are offered two single rooms for use, for example, as bedroom and sitting room.

23.10 Pre-existing care homes, which provided at least 80% of places in single rooms as at 16 August 2002 continue to do so. Where they did not provide that percentage of places in single rooms as at that date, they provide at least the same percentage of places in single rooms as they provided as at 31 March 2002.

Individual Accommodation: Furniture and Fittings

OUTCOME

Service users live in safe, comfortable bedrooms with their own possessions around them.

STANDARD 24

24.1 The home provides private accommodation for each service user which is furnished and equipped to assure comfort and privacy, and meets the assessed needs of the service user.

24.2 In the absence of service users' own provision, furnishings for individual rooms are provided to the minimum as follows:

- a clean comfortable bed, minimum 900mm wide, at a suitable, safe height for the service user, and bedlinen;
- curtains or blinds;
- mirror;
- overhead and bedside lighting;
- comfortable seating for two people;
- drawers and enclosed space for hanging clothes;
- at least 2 accessible double electric sockets;
- a table to sit at and a bed-side table;
- wash-hand basin (unless en-suite wc and whb provided).

24.3 Adjustable beds are provided for service users receiving nursing care.

24.4 The service user's room is carpeted or equivalent.

24.5 Doors to service users' private accommodation are fitted with locks suited to service users' capabilities and accessible to staff in emergencies.

24.6 Service users are provided with keys unless their risk assessment suggests otherwise.

24.7 Each service user has lockable storage space for medication, money and valuables and is provided with the key which he or she can retain (unless the reason for not doing so is explained in the care plan).

24.8 Screening is provided in double rooms to ensure privacy for personal care.

Services: Heating and Lighting

OUTCOME

Service users live in safe, comfortable surroundings.

STANDARD 25

25.1 The heating, lighting, water supply and ventilation of service users' accommodation meet the relevant environmental health and safety requirements and the needs of individual service users.

25.2 Rooms are individually and naturally ventilated with windows conforming to recognised standards.

25.3 In new build, extensions and all first time registrations the height of the window enables the service user to see out of it when seated or in bed.

25.4 Rooms are centrally heated and heating may be controlled in the service user's own room.

25.5 Pipe work and radiators are guarded or have guaranteed low temperature surfaces.

25.6 Lighting in service users' accommodation meets recognised standards (lux 150), is domestic in character, and includes table-level lamp lighting.

25.7 Emergency lighting is provided throughout the home

25.8 Water is stored at a temperature of at least 60oC and distributed at 50oC minimum, to prevent risks from Legionella. To prevent risks from scalding, pre-set valves of a type unaffected by changes in water pressure and which have fail safe devices are fitted locally to provide water close to 43oC.

Services: Hygiene and Control of Infection

OUTCOME

The home is clean, pleasant and hygienic.

STANDARD 26

26.1 The premises are kept clean, hygienic and free from offensive odours throughout and systems are in place to control the spread of infection, in accordance with relevant legislation and published professional guidance.

26.2 Laundry facilities are sited so that soiled articles, clothing and infected linen are not carried through areas where food is stored, prepared, cooked or eaten and do not intrude on service users.

26.3   Hand washing facilities are prominently sited in areas where infected material and/or clinical waste are being handled.

26.4   The laundry floor finishes are impermeable and these and wall finishes are readily cleanable.

26.5   Policies and procedures for control of infection include the safe handling and disposal of clinical waste; dealing with spillages; provision of protective clothing; hand washing.

26.6   The home has a sluicing facility and, in care homes providing nursing, a sluicing disinfector.

26.7   Foul laundry is washed at appropriate temperatures (minimum 65°C for not less than 10 minutes) to thoroughly clean linen and control risk of infection.

26.8   Washing machines have the specified programming ability to meet disinfection standards.

26.9   Services and facilities comply with the Water Supply (Water Fittings) Regulations 1999.

6

Staffing

INTRODUCTION TO STANDARDS 27 TO 30

The national minimum standards apply to the wide range of residential and nursing homes which exist in England. It is necessary to achieve a balance between drawing up standards which are specific enough to avoid the need for local negotiation, but which are broad enough to apply to the diverse nature of the clientele catered for (eg those who are physically frail; those who have dementia). Drawing up standards for staffing exemplifies some of the greatest difficulties of this kind. Where residents have a high level of physical dependency (in relation to capacity to perform the activities of daily living), staffing levels will need to reflect the needs of those residents. Where they require significant nursing attention, the skill mix of the staffing establishment must be adjusted accordingly. Residents with dementia also require care from appropriately skilled staff - and so on. In determining appropriate staffing establishments in all care homes, and in nursing care homes in particular, the regulatory requirement that staffing levels and skills mix are adequate to meet the assessed and recorded needs of the residents at all times in the particular home in question must be met.

This section, therefore, does not lay down detailed specifications for staffing to cover all situations but it does set out some baseline standards which should apply as minimum to all settings. Each home must then determine the appropriate staffing levels and skills to meet the assessed needs of its own particular residents, which will then be approved by the National Care Standards Commission (NCSC).

See: Burton, J (1998); Payne, C (1994); *Residential Forum* (1997).

Staff Complement

OUTCOME

Service users needs are met by the numbers and skill mix of staff.

STANDARD 27

27.1 **Staffing numbers and skill mix of qualified/unqualified staff are appropriate to the assessed needs of the service users, the size, layout and purpose of the home, at all times.**

27.2   A recorded staff rota showing which staff are on duty at any time during the day and night and in what capacity is kept.

27.3   The ratios of care staff to service users must be determined according to the assessed needs of residents, and a system operated for calculating staff numbers required, in accordance with guidance recommended by the Department of Health.

27.4   Additional staff are on duty at peak times of activity during the day.

27.5   There are waking night staff on duty in numbers that reflect the numbers and needs of service users and the layout of the home. In care homes providing nursing this includes registered nurse(s).

27.6   Staff providing personal care to service users are at least aged 18; staff left in charge of the home are at least aged 21.

27.7   Domestic staff are employed in sufficient numbers to ensure that standards relating to food, meals and nutrition are fully met, and that the home is maintained in a clean and hygienic state, free from dirt and unpleasant odours.

Qualifications

OUTCOME

Service users are in safe hands at all times.

STANDARD 28

28.1   A minimum ratio of 50% trained members of care staff (NVQ level 2 or equivalent) is achieved by 2005, excluding the registered manager and/or care manager, and in care homes providing nursing, excluding those members of the care staff who are registered nurses.

28.2   Any agency staff working in the home are included in the 50% ratio.

28.3   Trainees (including all staff under 18) are registered on a TOPSS-certified training programme.

Recruitment

OUTCOME

Service users are supported and protected by the home's recruitment policy and practices.

STANDARD 29

29.1 **The registered person operates a thorough recruitment procedure based on equal opportunities and ensuring the protection of service users.**

29.2 Two written references are obtained before appointing a member of staff, and any gaps in employment records are explored.

29.3 New staff are confirmed in post only following completion of a satisfactory police check, and satisfactory check of the Protection of Children and Vulnerable Adults and NMC registers.

29.4 Staff are employed in accordance with the code of conduct and practice set by the GSCC and are given copies of the code.

29.5 All staff receive statements of terms and conditions.

29.6 The recruitment and selection process for any volunteers involved in the home is thorough and includes police checks.

Staff Training

OUTCOME

Staff are trained and competent to do their jobs.

STANDARD 30

30.1 **The registered person ensures that there is a staff training and development programme which meets National Training Organisation (NTO) workforce training targets and ensures staff fulfil the aims of the home and meet the changing needs of service users.**

30.2 All members of staff receive induction training to NTO specification within 6 weeks of appointment to their posts, including training on the principles of care, safe working practices, the organisation and worker role, the experiences and particular needs of the service user group, and the influences and particular requirements of the service setting.

30.3 All staff receive foundation training to NTO specification within the first six months of appointment, which equips them to meet the assessed needs of the service users accommodated, as defined in their individual plan of care (see Standards 3 and 7).

30.4 All staff receive a minimum of three paid days training per year (including in house training), and have an individual training and development assessment and profile.

7

Management and Administration

INTRODUCTION TO STANDARDS 31 TO 38

The quality of care provided in a care home is strongly influenced by the calibre of the registered manager and their relationship with the registered provider (or owner) of the home, where these are not one and the same person.

This section sets out the standards relating to the qualities and qualifications required of the person in day to day control of the delivery of care, and how they should exercise their responsibilities.

Both the regulations and the standards highlight the importance of consulting service users about their health and personal care, interests and preferences. A competent, skilled manager is adept at fostering an atmosphere of openness and respect, in which residents, family, friends and staff all feel valued and that their opinions matter.

The requirement to have a quality assurance system formalises this process. It is not essential to subscribe to an external system, although many providers do and there are plenty of good examples to choose from. A key requirement of these standards is that service users are surveyed for their opinions and that the results of the survey are published.

See: *Inside Quality Assurance – The IQA Action Pack Centre for the Environment and Social Studies in Ageing* (1992); *Managing Residential Care*, Burton, J (1998)]

Day to Day Operations

OUTCOME

Service users live in a home which is run and managed by a person who is fit to be in charge, of good character and able to discharge his or her responsibilities fully.

STANDARD 31

31.1   The registered manager is qualified, competent and experienced to run the home and meet its stated purpose, aims and objectives.

31.2   The registered manager: has at least 2 years' experience in a senior management capacity in the managing of a relevant care setting within the past five years;

and

[by 2005], has a qualification, at level 4 NVQ, in management and care or equivalent;

or

where nursing care is provided by the home (ie nursing home), is a first level registered nurse, and has a relevant management qualification [by 2005].

31.3   The registered manager is responsible for no more than one registered establishment.

31.4   The registered manager can demonstrate that he/she has undertaken periodic training to update his/her knowledge, skills and competence, whilst managing the home.

31.5   The manager and other senior staff are familiar with the conditions/diseases associated with old age.

31.6   The job description of the registered manager enables him/her to take responsibility for fulfilling his/her duties.

31.7   There are clear lines of accountability within the home and with any external management.

31.8   Where the registered provider is in day-to-day control of the home, he/she meets all standards applying to the registered manager.

Ethos

OUTCOME

Service users benefit from the ethos, leadership and management approach of the home.

STANDARD 32

32.1   The registered manager ensures that the management approach of the home creates an open, positive and inclusive atmosphere.

32.2   The registered manager communicates a clear sense of direction and leadership which staff and service users understand and are able to relate to the aims and purpose of the home.

32.3   The registered manager has strategies for enabling staff, service users and other stakeholders to affect the way in which the service is delivered.

32.4   The processes of managing and running the home are open and transparent.

32.5   Management planning and practice encourage innovation, creativity and development.

32.6   A commitment is made to equal opportunities in the organisation.

32.7   The registered person complies with any Code of Practice published by the General Social Care Council, setting out standards expected of persons employing social care workers, insofar as the code is relevant to the management of a care home.

Quality Assurance

OUTCOME

The home is run in the best interests of service users.

STANDARD 33

33.1 **Effective quality assurance and quality monitoring systems, based on seeking the views of service users, are in place to measure success in meeting the aims, objectives and statement of purpose of the home.**

33.2 There is an annual development plan for the home, based on a systematic cycle of planning - action - review, reflecting aims and outcomes for service users.

33.3 There is continuous self-monitoring, using an objective, consistently obtained and reviewed and verifiable method (preferably a professionally recognised quality assurance system) and involving service users; and an internal audit takes place at least annually.

33.4 The results of service user surveys are published and made available to current and prospective users, their representatives and other interested parties, including the NCSC.

33.5 The registered manager and staff can demonstrate a commitment to lifelong learning and development for each service user, linked to implementation of his/her individual care plan.

33.6 Feedback is actively sought from service users about services provided through eg anonymous user satisfaction questionnaires and individual and group discussion, as well as evidence from records and life plans; and this informs all planning and reviews.

33.7 The views of family and friends and of stakeholders in the community (eg GPs, chiropodist, voluntary organisation staff) are sought on how the home is achieving goals for service users.

33.8 Service users are told about planned NCSC inspections and are given access to inspectors and the views of service users are made available to NCSC inspectors for inclusion in inspection reports.

33.9 Policies, procedures and practices are regularly reviewed in light of changing legislation and of good practice advice from the Department of Health, local/health authorities, and specialist / professional organisations.

33.10 Action is progressed within agreed timescales to implement requirements identified in NCSC inspection reports.

Financial Procedures

OUTCOME

Service users are safeguarded by the accounting and financial procedures of the home.

STANDARD 34

34.1 **Suitable accounting and financial procedures are adopted to demonstrate current financial viability and to ensure there is effective and efficient management of the business.**

34.2 Insurance cover is put in place against loss or damage to the assets of the business. The level of cover should reflect the full replacement value of buildings, fixture, fittings and equipment.

34.3 Insurance cover is provided for business interruption costs (including loss of earnings), as well as costs to the operator of meeting its contract liabilities. The latter must be sufficient to cover the registered person's legal liabilities to employees, service users and third party persons to a limit commensurate with the level and extent of activities undertaken or to a minimum of £5 million.

34.4 Records are kept of all transactions entered into by the registered person.

34.5 There is a business and financial plan for the establishment, open to inspection and reviewed annually.

Service Users' Money

OUTCOME

Service users' financial interests are safeguarded.

STANDARD 35

35.1 **The registered manager ensures that service users control their own money except where they state that they do not wish to or they lack capacity and that safeguards are in place to protect the interests of the service user.**

35.2 Written records of all transactions are maintained.

35.3 Where the money of individual service users is handled, the manager ensures that the personal allowances of these service users are not pooled and appropriate records and receipts are kept.

35.4 The registered manager may be appointed as agent for a service user only where no other individual is available. In this case, the manager ensures that:

- the registration authority is notified on inspection;

- records are kept of all incoming and outgoing payments.

If the manager is to be an appointee for social security purposes, the DSS is given appropriate notice.

35.5   Secure facilities are provided for the safe-keeping of money and valuables on behalf of the service user.

35.6   Records and receipts are kept of possessions handed over for safe keeping.

Staff Supervision

OUTCOME

Staff are appropriately supervised.

STANDARD 36

36.1   The registered person ensures that the employment policies and procedures adopted by the home and its induction, training and supervision arrangements are put into practice.

36.2   Care staff receive formal supervision at least 6 times a year.

36.3   Supervision covers:

- all aspects of practice;

- philosophy of care in the home;

- career development needs.

36.4   All other staff are supervised as part of the normal management process on a continuous basis.

36.5   Volunteers receive training, supervision and support appropriate to their role and do not replace paid staff.

Record Keeping

OUTCOME

Service users' rights and best interests are safeguarded by the home's record keeping policies and procedures.

STANDARD 37

37.1 **Records required by regulation for the protection of service users and for the effective and efficient running of the business are maintained, up to date and accurate.**

37.2 Service users have access to their records and information about them held by the home, as well as opportunities to help maintain their personal records.

37.3 Individual records and home records are secure, up to date and in good order; and are constructed, maintained and used in accordance with the Data Protection Act 1998 and other statutory requirements.

Safe Working Practices

OUTCOME

The health, safety and welfare of service users and staff are promoted and protected.

STANDARD 38

38.1 **The registered manager ensures so far as is reasonably practicable the health, safety and welfare of service users and staff.**

38.2 The registered manager ensures safe working practices including:

- moving and handling: use of techniques for moving people and objects that avoid injury to services users or staff;
- fire safety: understanding and implementation of appropriate fire procedures;
- first aid: knowledge of how to deal with accidents and health emergencies; provision of a first aid box and a qualified first aider at all times; and recording of all cases;
- food hygiene: correct storage and preparation of food to avoid food poisoning, including labelling and dating of stored food;
- infection control: understanding and practice of measures to prevent spread of infection and communicable diseases.

38.3 The registered manager ensures the health and safety of service users and staff including:

- safe storage and disposal of hazardous substances;
- regular servicing of boilers and central heating systems under contract by competent persons (eg members of Council of Registered Gas Installers (CORGI));
- maintenance of electrical systems and electrical equipment;
- regulation of water temperature, and design solutions to control:
- risk of Legionella,

- risks from hot water/surfaces (ie temperature close to 43°C);

- provision and maintenance of window restrictors, based on assessment of vulnerability of and risk to service users;

- maintenance of a safe environment including kitchen equipment and laundry machinery; outdoor steps and pathways; gardening equipment;

- security of the premises;

- security of service users based on an assessment of their vulnerability.

38.4 The registered manager ensures compliance with relevant legislation including:

- Health and Safety at Work Act 1974;

- Management of Health and Safety at Work Regulations 1999;

- Workplace (Health, Safety and Welfare) Regulations 1992;

- Provision and Use of Work Equipment Regulations 1992;

- Electricity at Work Regulations 1989;

- Health and Safety (First Aid) Regulations 1981;

- Control of Substances Hazardous to Health Regulations (COSHH) 1988;

- Manual Handling Operations Regulations 1992;

- Reporting of Injuries, Diseases and Dangerous Occurrences Regulations (RIDDOR)1985.

38.5 The registered manager provides a written statement of the policy, organisation and arrangements for maintaining safe working practices.

38.6 The registered manager ensures that risk assessments are carried out for all safe working practice topics and that significant findings of the risk assessment are recorded.

38.7 All accidents, injuries and incidents of illness or communicable disease are recorded and reported.

38.8 Safety procedures are posted, and explained, in formats that are easily understood and take account of service users' special communication needs.

38.9 All staff receive induction and foundation training and updates to meet TOPSS specification on all safe working practice topics (see Standard (30) Training).

Appendices

Glossary

Abuse

Single or repeated act or lack of appropriate action occurring within any relationship where there is an expectation of trust, which causes harm or distress to an older person [Action on Elder Abuse] including physical, emotional, verbal, financial, sexual, racial abuse, neglect and abuse through the misapplication of drugs.

Assessment

Collection and interpretation of data to determine an individual's need for health, personal and social care and support services, undertaken with the individual, his/her relatives/representatives, and relevant professionals.

Assisted Bath

A bath, with or without mechanism to vary height, which is designed to permit side or end access for a mobile hoist or other mechanism to allow a patient to be transferred from a bed, couch or trolley and raised or lowered into it.

(Where appropriate sufficient space is provided in bathrooms housing assisted baths to permit access into the room and movement within the room to allow these manoeuvres to be undertaken safely by staff.)

Care Home

An establishment providing accommodation with nursing or personal care.

Care Management

A system for organising the management and delivery of care services to vulnerable adults by local authority social services departments, and by Community Psychiatric Nurses (CPNs), psychiatrists and other NHS personnel under Care Program Approach (CPA) for people with mental health problems, involving assessing needs, care planning, organisation of care packages, monitoring and review, and close involvement with users and carers.

Care Management Care Plan

A written statement based on a single assessment process, setting out the health and social services care and support that a service user receives through Care Management, and how it is organised and delivered.

Care Programme Approach (CPA)

The formal process (integrated with Care Management) of assessing needs for services for people with mental health problems prior to and after discharge from hospital.

Contract

Written agreement between the service user and the home setting out the terms and conditions and rights and responsibilities of both parties, and including the Service User Plan.

First time registration

For the purposes of applying the standards, care homes which were in use immediately before April 2002 but were previously exempt from registration, such as "Royal Charter" homes and local authority homes, will NOT be treated as first time registrations and will only have to meet the "normal" standards.

Independent Advocate

An individual who is independent of the home, or of any of the statutory agencies involved in purchasing or provision of care in, or regulation of, the care home, who acts on behalf of, and in the interests of, a service user who feels unable to represent him/herself when dealing with professionals. Self-advocates are trained and supported to represent their own views.

Intermediate Care

A short period (normally no longer than six weeks) of intensive rehabilitation and treatment to enable service users to return home following (or to avoid) hospitalisation, or to prevent admission to long term residential care.

Keyworker

The person (who may be a designated nurse for people receiving nursing care) responsible for co-ordinating the service user's plan, for monitoring its progress and for staying in regular contact with the service user and everyone involved.

Outcome

The end result of the service provided by a care home to a service user, which can be used to measure the effectiveness of the service.

Personal Care

Care which includes assistance with bodily functions where required.

Physical Intervention

A method of responding to violence or aggressive behaviour which involves a degree of direct physical force to limit or restrict movement or mobility.

Policy

An operational statement of intent which helps staff make sound decisions and take actions which are legal, consistent with the aims of the home, and in the best interests of service users.

Pre-existing care home

For the purposes of applying the standards a pre-existing care home is one which existed immediately before 1 April 2002, whether or not registered under the Registered Homes Act 1984.

Procedure

The steps taken to fulfil a policy.

Registered Manager – see Registered Person

Registered Person

A person who either: carries on the home and is registered with the National Care Standards Commission to do so (the registered provider); or manages the home and is registered with the National Care Standards Commission to do so (the registered manager).

In some cases the registered provider may also manage the home.

Registered Provider – see Registered Person

Representative

A person acting on behalf of a service user, who may be a relative or friend.

Service User

Person living in and provided with services by a care home - a resident.

Service User's Plan

A Plan – generated from the Care Management assessment where applicable – developed by the home, with the service user and his or her relatives/representatives. The service user plan should cover all aspects of health and personal care, and show how these will be met in terms of daily living and longer term outcomes.

Staff

Person working for pay within or from the home, full time, part time, casual or contract.

Standard

A measure by which quality is judged.

TOPSS

The National Training Organisation for Social Care.

Usable Floor Space

Space which is accessible to the service user for furniture, possessions and daily living, with attention to e.g. room shape, positioning of doors, windows or en-suite facilities, and headroom.

Volunteers

People working without pay, or for expenses only, within or from the home.

Wheelchair User

A person whose main source of independent mobility is a wheelchair.

Bibliography

1 Choice of Home

Office of Fair Trading (1998) *Choosing a Care Home.* London: Office of Fair Trading.

2 Health and Personal Care

Royal College of Nursing (1997) *RCN Assessment Tool for Nursing Older People.* London:RCN.

Medication

Levenson, R (1998) *Drugs and Dementia: A Guide to Good Practice in the Use of Neuroleptic Drugs in Care Homes for Older People.* London: Age Concern England.

Royal College of Physician (1997) *Medication for Older People.* A Report of a Working Party of the Royal College of Physicians under the Chairmanship of M. J. Denham. London: Royal College of Physicians of London.

Royal Pharmaceutical Society of Great Britain (1991) *Pharmaceutical Services to Nursing Homes.* London: Royal Pharmaceutical Society of Great Britain.

UKCC (1992) *Standards for the Administration of Medicines.* London: UKCC.

Dying and Death

Counsel & Care (1995) Last Rights: *A Study of how Death and Dying are Handled in Residential Care and Nursing Homes.* London: Counsel & Care.

National Counsel for Hospice and Specialists Palliative Care Services (1997) *Changing Gear – Guidelines for Managing the Last Days of Life in Adults.* London: NCHSPC.

3 Daily Life and Social Activities

Benson, S (ed) (1998) *The Care Assistant's Guide to Working with People with Dementia.* London: RCN.

Clarke, A, Hollands, J, Smith, J (1996) Windows to a Damaged World; *Good Practice in Communicating with People with Dementia in Homes.* London: Counsel & Care.

Jewell, A (ed) (1998) Age Awareness: *Understanding the Spiritual Needs of Older People.* Derby: Methodist Homes for the Aged; Christian Council on Ageing.

Jones, A, Phillips, M, Maynard, C (1992) A Home from Home: *The Experience of Black Residential Projects as a Focus of Good Practice.* London: NISW; Race Equality Unit.

Marshall, M (1997) Dementia and Technology: *A Discussion of the Practical and Ethical Issues Surrounding the Use of Technology in Helping People with Dementia.* London: Counsel & Care.

Regan, D, Smith, J (1997) The Fullness of Time: *How Homes for Older People can Respond to their Residents' Need for Wholeness and a Spiritual Dimension to Care.* London: Counsel & Care.

Ward, C (1998) *Preparing for a Positive Future.* Chesterfield: Association for Residential Care.

Food and Mealtimes

Caroline Walker Trust (1995) *Eating Well for Older People: Practical and Nutritional Guidelines for Food in Residential and Nursing Homes and for Community Meals.* London: Caroline Walker Trust.

VOICES (1998) *Eating Well for Older People with Dementia: A Good Practice Guide for Residential and Nursing Homes and Others Involved in Caring for Older People with Dementia.* Potters Bar: VOICES; Gardner Merchant Healthcare Services.

4 Complaints and Protection

Abuse and Restraint

Action on Elder Abuse (1994) Elder Abuse in Care Homes: *Who to Contact and What To Do* . London: Action on Elder Abuse.

Association of Directors of Social Services (1995) *Mistreatment of Older People.* Northallerton: ADSS.

Royal College of Nursing (1996) *Combating Elder Abuse and Neglect of Older People.* RCN Guidelines for Nurses: London: RCN.

Department of Health and Home Office (2000) *No secrets: guidance on developing and implementing multi-agency policies and procedures to protect vulnerable adults from abuse:* London: Department of Health.

Department of Health (2000) *Draft guidance on the use of physical interventions for staff working with children and adults with learning disability and/or autism:* London: Department of Health.

5 Environment

Centre for Accessible Environments (1998) *The Design of Residential and Nursing Homes for Older People (Health Facilities Notes HFN19).* Leeds: NHS Estates on behalf of the Centre for Accessible Environments.

Department of Health and Social Security; Welsh Office (1973) *Residential Accommodation for Elderly People. Local Authority Building Note No. 2 revised edition.* London: HMSO.

Peace, S, Kellaher, L and Willcocks, D (1982) *A Balanced Life? A Consumer Study of Residential Life in One Hundred Local Authority Old People's Homes,* Research report No. 14, Social Research Unit, Polytechnic of North London.

Torrington, J (1996) *Care Homes for Older People,* London: E&FN Spon.

Public Health Medicine Environment Group (1996) *Guidelines on the Control of Infection in Residential and Nursing Homes,* London: Department of Health.

6 Staffing

Centre for Policy on Ageing (1994) *Home Ground: How to Select and Get the Best Out of Staff: A Home-based Scheme Designed for the Managers and Heads of Residential Care Homes.* London: CPA.

Residential Forum (1998) *Training for Social Care: Achieving Standards for the Undervalued Service: A Report on the Training and Staff Development for People Working in the Residential Care of Adults.* London: NISW.

7 Management and Administration

Burton, J (1998) *Managing Residential Care,* London: Routledge.

Centre for Environmental and Social Studies in Ageing (1992) *Inside Quality Assurance - the IQA Pack,* London: Centre for the Environmental and Social Studies in Ageing: CESSA, Information Design Unit.

Payne, C (1994) *Evaluating Quality of Care,* London: NSW.

Residential Forum (1997) *Managing 'A Home from Home': a Companion to 'Creating a Home from Home' - A Guide to Standards.* London: Residential Forum.

Safety at Work

Health and Safety Executive (1993) *Health and Safety in Residential Care Homes (HS(G)104).* Sudbury: Health and Safety Executive.

General Good Practice Guides

Centre for Policy on Ageing (1984) *Home Life: A Code of Good Practice*, Report of a Working Party sponsored by the Department of Health and Social Security and convened by the Centre for Policy on Ageing under the chairmanship of Kina, Lady Avebury. London: Centre for Policy on Ageing.

Centre for Policy on Ageing (1996) *A Better Home Life: A Code of Good Practice for Residential and Nursing Home Care*, Report of an Advisory Group convened by the Centre for Policy on Ageing under the chairmanship of Kina, Lady Avebury. London: Centre for Policy on Ageing.

Department of Health (1989) *Homes are For Living In: A Model for Evaluating Quality of Care Provided, and Quality of Life Experienced, in Residential Care Homes for Elderly People*. Social Services Inspectorate. London: HMSO.

National Association of Health Authorities [and Trusts] (1985) *Registration and Inspection of Nursing Homes: A Handbook for Health Authorities Supplement*. Birmingham: NAHAT.

National Association of Health Authorities and Trusts (1999) *Registration and Inspection of Nursing Homes: A Handbook for Health Authorities Supplement*. Birmingham: NAHAT.

Residential Forum (1996) *Create a Home from Home: A Guide to Standards*. London: NISW.

Other References

Department of Health (1998) Modernising Social Services: *Promoting Independence, Improving Protection, Raising Standards*. London: HMSO.

Department of Health (2000) *Care Standards Act 2000*. London: HMSO.

Note: the Regulations printed here have been edited so as to incorporate amendments made by S.I. 2002 No. 865.

STATUTORY INSTRUMENTS

2001 No. 3965

SOCIAL CARE, ENGLAND
CHILDREN AND YOUNG PERSONS, ENGLAND

The Care Homes Regulations 2001

Made	*11th December 2001*
Laid before Parliament	*12th December 2001*
Coming into force	*1st April 2002*

ARRANGEMENT OF REGULATIONS

PART I
GENERAL

PART II
REGISTERED PERSONS

PART III
CONDUCT OF CARE HOMES

The Secretary of State, in exercise of the powers conferred upon him by sections 3(3), 22(1), (2)(a) to (d) and (f) to (j), (5), (7)(a) to (h), (j) and (l), 25(1), 34(1), 35 and 118(5) to (7) of the Care Standards Act 2000[1], and of all other powers enabling him in that behalf, having consulted such persons as he considers appropriate[2], hereby makes the following Regulations:

PART I

GENERAL

Citation, commencement and extent

1. - (1) These Regulations may be cited as the Care Homes Regulations 2001 and shall come into force on 1st April 2002.

(2) These Regulations extend to England only.

Interpretation

2. - (1) In these Regulations -

"the Act" means the Care Standards Act 2000;
"environmental health authority" means the authority responsible for environmental health for the area in which the care home is situated;
"fire authority", in relation to a care home, means the authority discharging in the area in which the care home is situated the function of fire authority under the Fire Services Act 1947[3];
"general practitioner" means a registered medical practitioner who -

(a) provides general medical services under Part II of the National Health Service Act 1977[4];

(b) performs personal medical services in connection with a pilot scheme under the National Health Service (Primary Care) Act 1997[5]; or

(c) provides services which correspond to services provided under Part II of the National Health Service Act 1977, otherwise than in pursuance of that Act;

"health care professional" means a person who is registered as a member of any profession to which section 60(2) of the Health Act 1999[6] applies or who is clinical psychologist, child psychotherapist or speech therapist;
"inspection report" means a report prepared in relation to the care home under section 32(5) of the Act;
"organisation" means a body corporate or any unincorporated association other than a partnership;

"registered manager", in relation to a care home, means a person who is registered under Part II of the Act as the manager of the care home;

"registered person", in relation to a care home, means any person who is the registered provider or registered manager in respect of the care home;

"registered provider", in relation to a care home, means a person who is registered under Part II of the Act as a person carrying on the care home;

"relative", in relation to any person, means -

(a) the person's spouse;

(b) any parent, grandparent, child, grandchild, brother, sister, uncle, aunt, nephew or niece of his or his spouse;

(c) the spouse of any relative within sub-paragraph (b) of this definition,

and for the purpose of determining any such relationship a person's step-child shall be treated as his child, and references to "spouse" in relation to any person include a former spouse and a person who is living with the person as husband and wife;

"representative" means, in relation to a service user, a person, other than the registered person or a person employed at the care home, who with the service user's express or implied consent takes an interest in the service user's health and welfare;

"responsible individual" shall be construed in accordance with regulation 7(2)(c)(i);

"service user" means any person accommodated in the care home who is in need of nursing or personal care by reason of disability, infirmity, past or present illness, past or present mental disorder or past or present dependence on alcohol or drugs;

"service user's guide" means the written guide produced in accordance with regulation 5(1);

"service user's plan" means the written plan prepared in accordance with regulation 15(1);

"staff" means persons employed by the registered person to work at the care home but does not include a volunteer or a person employed under a contract for services;

"statement of purpose" means the written statement compiled in accordance with regulation 4(1).

(2) In these Regulations, unless the context otherwise requires, a reference -

(a) to a numbered regulation or Schedule is to the regulation in, or Schedule to, these Regulations bearing that number;

(b) in a regulation or Schedule to a numbered paragraph is to the paragraph in that regulation or Schedule bearing that number;

(c) in a paragraph to a lettered or numbered sub-paragraph is to the sub-paragraph in that paragraph bearing that letter or number.

(3) In these Regulations, references to employing a person include employing a person whether or not for payment and whether under a contract of service or a contract for services and allowing a person to work as a volunteer; and references to an employee or to a person being employed shall be construed accordingly.

Excepted establishments

3. - (1) For the purposes of the Act, an establishment is excepted from being a care home if -

(a) it is a health service hospital at which nursing is provided;

(b) it provides accommodation, together with nursing, and is vested -

(i) in the Secretary of State for the purposes of his functions under the National Health Service Act 1977[7]; or

(ii) in an NHS trust[8];

(c) it is a university;

(d) it is an institution within the further education sector as defined by section 91(3) of the Further and Higher Education Act 1992[9]; or

(e) it is a school.

(2) For the purposes of paragraph (1), "university" includes -

(a) any university college;

(b) any college, or institution in the nature of a college, of a university.

(3) The exception in paragraph (1)(d) does not apply if -

(a) the establishment provides accommodation together with nursing or personal care to any person; and

(b) the number of such persons is more than one tenth of the number of students to whom it provides both education and accommodation.

Statement of purpose

4. - (1) The registered person shall compile in relation to the care home a written statement (in these Regulations referred to as "the statement of purpose") which shall consist of -

(a) a statement of the aims and objectives of the care home;

(b) a statement as to the facilities and services which are to be provided by the registered person for service users; and

(c) a statement as to the matters listed in Schedule 1.

(2) The registered person shall supply a copy of the statement of purpose to the Commission and shall make a copy of it available on request for inspection by every service user and any representative of a service user.

(3) Nothing in regulation 16(1) or 23(1) shall require or authorise the registered person to contravene, or not to comply with -

(a) any other provision of these Regulations; or

(b) the conditions for the time being in force in relation to the registration of the registered person under Part II of the Act.

Service user's guide

5. - (1) The registered person shall produce a written guide to the care home (in these Regulations referred to as "the service user's guide") which shall include -

(a) a summary of the statement of purpose;

(b) the terms and conditions in respect of accommodation to be provided for service users, including as to the amount and method of payment of fees;

(c) a standard form of contract for the provision of services and facilities by the registered provider to service users;

(d) the most recent inspection report;

(e) a summary of the complaints procedure established under regulation 22;

(f) the address and telephone number of the Commission.

(2) The registered person shall supply a copy of the service user's guide to the Commission and each service user.

(3) Where a local authority has made arrangements for the provision of accommodation, nursing or personal care to the service user at the care home, the registered person shall supply to the service user a copy of the agreement specifying the arrangements made.

Review of statement of purpose and service user's guide

6. The registered person shall -

(a) keep under review and, where appropriate, revise the statement of purpose and the service user's guide; and

(b) notify the Commission and service users of any such revision within 28 days.

PART II

REGISTERED PERSONS

Fitness of registered provider

7. - (1) A person shall not carry on a care home unless he is fit to do so.

(2) A person is not fit to carry on a care home unless the person -

(a) is an individual who carries on the care home -

   (i) otherwise than in partnership with others, and he satisfies the requirements set out in paragraph (3);

   (ii) in partnership with others, and he and each of his partners satisfies the requirements set out in paragraph (3);

(b) is a partnership, and each of the partners satisfies the requirements set out in paragraph (3);

(c) is an organisation and -

   (i) the organisation has given notice to the Commission of the name, address and position in the organisation of an individual (in these Regulations referred to as "the responsible individual") who is a director, manager, secretary or other officer of the organisation and is responsible for supervising the management of the care home; and

   (ii) that individual satisfies the requirements set out in paragraph (3).

(3) The requirements are that -

(a) he is of integrity and good character; and

(b) he is physically and mentally fit to carry on the care home; and

(c) full and satisfactory information is available in relation to him in respect of the following matters -

   (i) the matters specified in paragraphs 1 to 5 and 7 of Schedule 2;

(5) A person shall not carry on a care home if -

(a) he has been adjudged bankrupt or sequestration of his estate has been awarded and (in either case) he has not been discharged and the bankruptcy order has not been annulled or rescinded; or

(b) he has made a composition or arrangement with his creditors and has not been discharged in respect of it.

Appointment of manager

8. - (1) The registered provider shall appoint an individual to manage the care home where -

(a) there is no registered manager in respect of the care home; and

(b) the registered provider -

   (i) is an organisation or partnership;

   (ii) is not a fit person to manage a care home; or

(iii) is not, or does not intend to be, in full-time day to day charge of the care home.

(2) Where the registered provider appoints a person to manage the care home he shall forthwith give notice to the Commission of -

(a) the name of the person so appointed; and

(b) the date on which the appointment is to take effect.

Fitness of registered manager

9. - (1) A person shall not manage a care home unless he is fit to do so.

(2) A person is not fit to manage a care home unless -

(a) he is of integrity and good character;

(b) having regard to the size of the care home, the statement of purpose, and the number and needs of the service users -

(i) he has the qualifications, skills and experience necessary for managing the care home; and

(ii) he is physically and mentally fit to manage the care home; and

(c) full and satisfactory information is available in relation to him in respect of the following matters -

(i) the matters specified in paragraphs 1 to 5 and 7 of Schedule 2;

Registered person: general requirements

10. - (1) The registered provider and the registered manager shall, having regard to the size of the care home, the statement of purpose, and the number and needs of the service users, carry on or manage the care home (as the case may be) with sufficient care, competence and skill.

(2) If the registered provider is -

(a) an individual, he shall undertake;

(b) an organisation, it shall ensure that the responsible individual undertakes;

(c) a partnership, it shall ensure that one of the partners undertakes,

from time to time such training as is appropriate to ensure that he has the experience and skills necessary for carrying on the care home.

(3) The registered manager shall undertake from time to time such training as is appropriate to ensure that he has the experience and skills necessary for managing the care home.

Notification of offences

11. Where the registered person or the responsible individual is convicted of any criminal offence, whether in England and Wales or elsewhere, he shall forthwith give notice in writing to the Commission of -

(a) the date and place of the conviction;

(b) the offence of which he was convicted; and

(c) the penalty imposed on him in respect of the offence.

PART III

CONDUCT OF CARE HOME

Health and welfare of service users

12. - (1) The registered person shall ensure that the care home is conducted so as -

(a) to promote and make proper provision for the health and welfare of service users;

(b) to make proper provision for the care and, where appropriate, treatment, education and supervision of service users.

(2) The registered person shall so far as practicable enable service users to make decisions with respect to the care they are to receive and their health and welfare.

(3) The registered person shall, for the purpose of providing care to service users, and making proper provision for their health and welfare, so far as practicable ascertain and take into account their wishes and feelings.

(4) The registered person shall make suitable arrangements to ensure that the care home is conducted -

(a) in a manner which respects the privacy and dignity of service users;

(b) with due regard to the sex, religious persuasion, racial origin, and cultural and linguistic background and any disability of service users.

(5) The registered provider and registered manager (if any) shall, in relation to the conduct of the care home -

(a) maintain good personal and professional relationships with each other and with service users and staff; and

(b) encourage and assist staff to maintain good personal and professional relationships with service users.

Further requirements as to health and welfare

13. - (1) The registered person shall make arrangements for service users -

(a) to be registered with a general practitioner of their choice; and

(b) to receive where necessary, treatment, advice and other services from any health care professional.

(2) The registered person shall make arrangements for the recording, handling, safekeeping, safe administration and disposal of medicines received into the care home.

(3) The registered person shall make suitable arrangements to prevent infection, toxic conditions and the spread of infection at the care home.

(4) The registered person shall ensure that -

(a) all parts of the home to which service users have access are so far as reasonably practicable free from hazards to their safety;

(b) any activities in which service users participate are so far as reasonably practicable free from avoidable risks; and

(c) unnecessary risks to the health or safety of service users are identified and so far as possible eliminated,

and shall make suitable arrangements for the training of staff in first aid.

(5) The registered person shall make suitable arrangements to provide a safe system for moving and handling service users.

(6) The registered person shall make arrangements, by training staff or by other measures, to prevent service users being harmed or suffering abuse or being placed at risk of harm or abuse.

(7) The registered person shall ensure that no service user is subject to physical restraint unless restraint of the kind employed is the only practicable means of securing the welfare of that or any other service user and there are exceptional circumstances.

(8) On any occasion on which a service user is subject to physical restraint, the registered person shall record the circumstances, including the nature of the restraint.

Assessment of service users

14. - (1) The registered person shall not provide accommodation to a service user at the care home unless, so far as it shall have been practicable to do so -

(a) needs of the service user have been assessed by a suitably qualified or suitably trained person;

(b) the registered person has obtained a copy of the assessment;

(c) there has been appropriate consultation regarding the assessment with the service user or a representative of the service user;

(d) the registered person has confirmed in writing to the service user that having regard to the assessment the care home is suitable for the purpose of meeting the service user's needs in respect of his health and welfare.

(2) The registered person shall ensure that the assessment of the service user's needs is -

(a) kept under review; and

(b) revised at any time when it is necessary to do so having regard to any change of circumstances.

Service user's plan

15. - (1) Unless it is impracticable to carry out such consultation, the registered person shall, after consultation with the service user, or a representative of his, prepare a written plan ("the service user's plan") as to how the service user's needs in respect of his health and welfare are to be met.

(2) The registered person shall -

(a) make the service user's plan available to the service user;

(b) keep the service user's plan under review;

(c) where appropriate and, unless it is impracticable to carry out such consultation, after consultation with the service user or a representative of his, revise the service user's plan; and

(d) notify the service user of any such revision.

Facilities and services

16. - (1) Subject to regulation 4(3), the registered person shall provide facilities and services to service users in accordance with the statement required by regulation 4(1)(b) in respect of the care home.

(2) The registered person shall having regard to the size of the care home and the number and needs of service users -

(a) provide, so far as is necessary for the purpose of managing the care home -

(i) appropriate telephone facilities;

(ii) appropriate facilities for communication by facsimile transmission;

(b) provide telephone facilities which are suitable for the needs of service users, and make arrangements to enable service users to use such facilities in private;

(c) provide in rooms occupied by service users adequate furniture, bedding and other furnishings, including curtains and floor coverings, and equipment suitable to the needs of service users and screens where necessary;

(d) permit service users, so far as it is practicable to do so, to bring their own furniture and furnishings into the rooms they occupy;

(e) arrange for the regular laundering of linen and clothing;

(f) so far as it is practicable to do so, provide adequate facilities for service users to wash, dry and iron their own clothes if they so wish and, for that purpose, to make arrangements for their clothes to be sorted and kept separately;

(g) provide sufficient and suitable kitchen equipment, crockery, cutlery and utensils, and adequate facilities for the preparation and storage of food;

(h) provide adequate facilities for service users to prepare their own food and ensure that such facilities are safe for use by service users;

(i) provide, in adequate quantities, suitable, wholesome and nutritious food which is varied and properly prepared and available at such time as may reasonably be required by service users;

(j) after consultation with the environmental health authority, make suitable arrangements for maintaining satisfactory standards of hygiene in the care home;

(k) keep the care home free from offensive odours and make suitable arrangements for the disposal of general and clinical waste;

(l) provide a place where the money and valuables of service users may be deposited for safe keeping, and make arrangements for service users to acknowledge in writing the return to them of any money or valuables so deposited;

(m) consult service users about their social interests, and make arrangements to enable them to engage in local, social and community activities and to visit, or maintain contact or communicate with, their families and friends;

(n) consult service users about the programme of activities arranged by or on behalf of the care home, and provide facilities for recreation including, having regard to the needs of service users, activities in relation to recreation, fitness and training.

(3) The registered person shall ensure that so far as practicable service users have the opportunity to attend religious services of their choice.

(4) In this regulation "food" includes drink.

Records

17. - (1) The registered person shall -

(a) maintain in respect of each service user a record which includes the information, documents and other records specified in Schedule 3 relating to the service user;

(b) ensure that the record referred to in sub-paragraph (a) is kept securely in the care home.

(2) The registered person shall maintain in the care home the records specified in Schedule 4.

(3) The registered person shall ensure that the records referred to in paragraphs (1) and (2) -

(a) are kept up to date; and

(b) are at all times available for inspection in the care home by any person authorised by the Commission to enter and inspect the care home.

(4) The records referred to in paragraphs (1) and (2) shall be retained for not less than three years from the date of the last entry.

Staffing

18. - (1) The registered person shall, having regard to the size of the care home, the statement of purpose and the number and needs of service users -

(a) ensure that at all times suitably qualified, competent and experienced persons are working at the care home in such numbers as are appropriate for the health and welfare of service users;

(b) ensure that the employment of any persons on a temporary basis at the care home will not prevent service users from receiving such continuity of care as is reasonable to meet their needs;

(c) ensure that the persons employed by the registered person to work at the care home receive -

(i) training appropriate to the work they are to perform; and

(ii) suitable assistance, including time off, for the purpose of obtaining further qualifications appropriate to such work.

(2) The registered person shall ensure that persons working at the care home are appropriately supervised.

(3) Where the care home -

(a) provides nursing to service users; and

(b) provides, whether or not in connection with nursing, medicines or medical treatment to service users,

the registered person shall ensure that at all times a suitably qualified registered nurse is working at the care home.

(4) The registered person shall make arrangements for providing persons who work at the care home with appropriate information about any code of practice published under section 62 of the

Act.

Fitness of workers

19. - (1) The registered person shall not employ a person to work at the care home unless -

(a) the person is fit to work at the care home;

(b) subject to paragraph (6), he has obtained in respect of that person the information and documents specified in -

(i) paragraphs 1 to 7 of Schedule 2;

(c) he is satisfied on reasonable grounds as to the authenticity of the references referred to in paragraph 5 of Schedule 2 in respect of that person.

(2) This paragraph applies to a person who is employed by a person ("the employer") other than the registered person.

(3) This paragraph applies to a position in which a person may in the course of his duties have regular contact with service users at the care home or with any other person of a description specified in section 3(2) of the Act.

(4) The registered person shall not allow a person to whom paragraph (2) applies to work at the care home in a position to which paragraph (3) applies, unless -

(a) the person is fit to work at the care home;

(b) the employer has obtained in respect of that person the information and documents specified in -

(i) paragraphs 1 to 7 of Schedule 2;

and has confirmed in writing to the registered person that he has done so; and

(c) the employer is satisfied on reasonable grounds as to the authenticity of the references referred to in paragraph 5 of Schedule 2 in respect of that person, and has confirmed in writing to the registered person that he is so satisfied.

(5) For the purposes of paragraphs (1) and (4), a person is not fit to work at a care home unless -

(a) he is of integrity and good character;

(b) he has qualifications suitable to the work that he is to perform, and the skills and experience necessary for such work;

(c) he is physically and mentally fit for the purposes of the work which he is to perform at the care home; and

(d) full and satisfactory information is available in relation to him in respect of the following matters -

> (i) each of the matters specified in paragraphs 1 to 6 of Schedule 2;

> (ii) except where paragraph (7) applies, each of the matters specified in paragraph 7 of that Schedule;

> (iii) where paragraph (7) applies, each of the matters specified in paragraph 8 of that Schedule.

(6) Paragraphs (1)(b) and (5)(d), in so far as they relate to paragraph 7 of Schedule 2, shall not apply until 1st April 2003 in respect of a person who immediately before 1st April 2002 is employed to work at the care home.

Restrictions on acting for service user

20. - (1) Subject to paragraph (2), the registered person shall not pay money belonging to any service user into a bank account unless -

> (a) the account is in the name of the service user, or any of the service users, to which the money belongs; and

> (b) the account is not used by the registered person in connection with the carrying on or management of the care home.

(2) Paragraph (1) does not apply to money which is paid to the registered person in respect of charges payable by a service user for accommodation or other services provided by the registered person at the care home.

(3) The registered person shall ensure so far as practicable that persons working at the care home do not act as the agent of a service user.

Staff views as to conduct of care home

21. - (1) This regulation applies to any matter relating to the conduct of the care home so far as it may affect the health or welfare of service users.

(2) The registered person shall make arrangements to enable staff to inform the registered person and the Commission of their views about any matter to which this regulation applies.

Complaints

22. - (1) The registered person shall establish a procedure ("the complaints procedure") for considering complaints made to the registered person by a service user or person acting on the service user's behalf.

(2) The complaints procedure shall be appropriate to the needs of service users.

(3) The registered person shall ensure that any complaint made under the complaints procedure is fully investigated.

(4) The registered person shall, within 28 days after the date on which the complaint is made, or such shorter period as may be reasonable in the circumstances, inform the person who made the complaint of the action (if any) that is to be taken.

(5) The registered person shall supply a written copy of the complaints procedure to every service user and to any person acting on behalf of a service user if that person so requests.

(6) Where a written copy of the complaints procedure is to be supplied in accordance with paragraph (5) to a person who is blind or whose vision is impaired, the registered person shall so far as it is practicable to do so supply, in addition to the written copy, a copy of the complaints procedure in a form which is suitable for that person.

(7) The copy of the complaints procedure to be supplied in accordance with paragraphs (5) and (6) shall include -

   (a) the name, address and telephone number of the Commission; and

   (b) the procedure (if any) that has been notified by the Commission to the registered person for the making of complaints to the Commission relating to the care home.

(8) The registered person shall supply to the Commission at its request a statement containing a summary of the complaints made during the preceding twelve months and the action that was taken in response.

PART IV

PREMISES

Fitness of premises

23. - (1) Subject to regulation 4(3), the registered person shall not use premises for the purposes of a care home unless -

   (a) the premises are suitable for the purpose of achieving the aims and objectives set out in the statement of purpose; and

   (b) the location of the premises is appropriate to the needs of service users.

(2) The registered person shall having regard to the number and needs of the service users ensure that -

   (a) the physical design and layout of the premises to be used as the care home meet the needs of the service users;

   (b) the premises to be used as the care home are of sound construction and kept in a good state of repair externally and internally;

   (c) equipment provided at the care home for use by service users or persons who work at the care home is maintained in good working order;

(d) all parts of the care home are kept clean and reasonably decorated;

(e) adequate private and communal accommodation is provided for service users;

(f) the size and layout of rooms occupied or used by service users are suitable for their needs;

(g) there is adequate sitting, recreational and dining space provided separately from the service user's private accommodation;

(h) the communal space provided for service users is suitable for the provision of social, cultural and religious activities appropriate to the circumstances of service users;

(i) suitable facilities are provided for service users to meet visitors in communal accommodation, and in private accommodation which is separate from the service users' own private rooms;

(j) there are provided at appropriate places in the premises sufficient numbers of lavatories, and of wash-basins, baths and showers fitted with a hot and cold water supply;

(k) any necessary sluicing facilities are provided;

(l) suitable provision is made for storage for the purposes of the care home;

(m) suitable storage facilities are provided for the use of service users;

(n) suitable adaptations are made, and such support, equipment and facilities, including passenger lifts, as may be required are provided, for service users who are old, infirm or physically disabled;

(o) external grounds which are suitable for, and safe for use by, service users are provided and appropriately maintained;

(p) ventilation, heating and lighting suitable for service users is provided in all parts of the care home which are used by service users.

(3) The registered person shall provide for staff -

(a) suitable facilities and accommodation, other than sleeping accommodation, including -

(i) facilities for the purpose of changing;

(ii) storage facilities;

(b) sleeping accommodation where the provision of such accommodation is needed by staff in connection with their work at the care home.

(4) The registered person shall after consultation with the fire authority -

(a) take adequate precautions against the risk of fire, including the provision of suitable fire equipment;

(b) provide adequate means of escape;

(c) make adequate arrangements -

(i) for detecting, containing and extinguishing fires;

(ii) for giving warnings of fires;

(iii) for the evacuation, in the event of fire, of all persons in the care home and safe placement of service users;

(iv) for the maintenance of all fire equipment; and

(v) for reviewing fire precautions, and testing fire equipment, at suitable intervals;

(d) make arrangements for persons working at the care home to receive suitable training in fire prevention; and

(e) to ensure, by means of fire drills and practices at suitable intervals, that the persons working at the care home and, so far as practicable, service users, are aware of the procedure to be followed in case of fire, including the procedure for saving life.

(5) The registered person shall undertake appropriate consultation with the authority responsible for environmental health for the area in which the care home is situated.

PART V

MANAGEMENT

Review of quality of care

24. - (1) The registered person shall establish and maintain a system for -

(a) reviewing at appropriate intervals; and

(b) improving,

the quality of care provided at the care home, including the quality of nursing where nursing is provided at the care home.

(2) The registered person shall supply to the Commission a report in respect of any review conducted by him for the purposes of paragraph (1), and make a copy of the report available to service users.

(3) The system referred to in paragraph (1) shall provide for consultation with service users and their representatives.

Financial position

25. - (1) The registered provider shall carry on the care home in such manner as is likely to ensure that the care home will be financially viable for the purpose of achieving the aims and objectives set out in the statement of purpose.

(2) The registered person shall, if the Commission so requests, provide the Commission with such information and documents as it may require for the purpose of considering the financial viability of the care home, including -

(a) the annual accounts of the care home certified by an accountant;

(b) a reference from a bank expressing an opinion as to the registered provider's financial standing;

(c) information as to the financing and financial resources of the care home;

(d) where the registered provider is a company, information as to any of its associated companies;

(e) a certificate of insurance for the registered provider in respect of liability which may be incurred by him in relation to the care home in respect of death, injury, public liability, damage or other loss.

(3) The registered person shall -

(a) ensure that adequate accounts are maintained in respect of the care home and kept up to date;

(b) ensure that the accounts give details of the running costs of the care home, including rent, payments under a mortgage and expenditure on food, heating and salaries and wages of staff; and

(c) supply a copy of the accounts to the Commission at its request.

(4) In this regulation a company is an associated company of another if one of them has control of the other or both are under the control of the same person.

Visits by registered provider

26. - (1) Where the registered provider is an individual, but not in day to day charge of the care home, he shall visit the care home in accordance with this regulation.

(2) Where the registered provider is an organisation or partnership, the care home shall be visited in accordance with this regulation by -

(a) the responsible individual or one of the partners, as the case may be;

(b) another of the directors or other persons responsible for the management of the organisation or partnership; or

(c) an employee of the organisation or the partnership who is not directly concerned with the conduct of the care home.

(3) Visits under paragraph (1) or (2) shall take place at least once a month and shall be unannounced.

(4) The person carrying out the visit shall -

(a) interview, with their consent and in private, such of the service users and their representatives and persons working at the care home as appears necessary in order to form an opinion of the standard of care provided in the care home;

(b) inspect the premises of the care home, its record of events and records of any complaints; and

(c) prepare a written report on the conduct of the care home.

(5) The registered provider shall supply a copy of the report required to be made under paragraph (4)(c) to -

(a) the Commission;

(b) the registered manager; and

(c) in the case of a visit under paragraph (2) -

(i) where the registered provider is an organisation, to each of the directors or other persons responsible for the management of the organisation; and

(ii) where the registered provider is a partnership, to each of the partners.

PART VI

CHILDREN

Application of this Part

27. The provisions of this Part shall apply where any child is accommodated in the care home.

Interpretation

28. In regulation 2, paragraph (1) shall have effect as if -

(a) at the end of the definition of "service user" there were added the words ", or any child who is accommodated in the care home";

(b) the following definitions were added at the appropriate places -

" "placement plan" has the meaning given to it in regulation 12 (child's placement plan) of the Children's Homes Regulations 2001[10];

"placing authority" has the meaning given to it in regulation 2(1) (interpretation) of the Children's Homes Regulations 2001;".

Statement of purpose

29. In regulation 4, paragraph (1) shall have effect as if at the end of that paragraph there were added the following -

" and
(d) the information specified in Schedule 5.".

Registered person

30. - (1) In regulation 7, paragraph (3) shall have effect as if at the end of that paragraph there were added the following -

> " and
> (d) his skills and experience are suitable for the purpose of his working with children.".

(2) In regulation 9, paragraph (2) shall have effect as if at the end of that paragraph there were added the following -

> " and
> (d) his skills and experience are suitable for the purpose of his working with children and either -
>
> > (i) his qualifications are suitable for the purpose of his working with children; or
> >
> > (ii) another person has been appointed for the purpose of assisting him in the management of the care home, and the qualifications of the person so appointed are suitable for the purpose of his working with children.".

(3) In regulation 10, paragraph (1) shall have effect as if for the words "and the number and needs of the service users," there were substituted the words "the number and needs of the service users and the need to safeguard and promote the welfare of children accommodated in the care home,".

Separate provision for children

31. - (1) Subject to paragraph (2), the registered person shall ensure that -

(a) the provision to be made for the care, treatment and supervision of children accommodated in the care home; and

(b) the provision of facilities and services to them,

shall, so far as it is practicable to do so, be made separately from other service users.

(2) Paragraph (1) shall not prevent the registered person from making provision jointly for children and other service users whose age does not significantly differ from those children.

Welfare and protection of children

32. - (1) Regulation 12 of these Regulations shall have effect as if, at the end of sub-paragraph (a) of paragraph (1) of that regulation there were added the words ", including provision for safeguarding the welfare of children accommodated in the care home".

(2) The provisions of regulations 12, 15 to 18, 23 and 30 of, and Schedule 5 to, the Children's Homes Regulations 2001 (child's placement plan; contact and access to communications; arrangements for the protection of children; behaviour management, discipline and restraint;

education, employment and leisure activity; hazards and safety; notifiable events) shall apply to the registered person as if -

(a) any reference to the registered person were to the registered person as defined in these Regulations;

(b) any reference to the children's home or the home were to the care home.

(3) Where the registered person notifies the Commission in accordance with regulation 30 of the Children's Homes Regulations 2001 of any of the following events, namely -

(a) serious illness or a serious accident sustained by a child accommodated at the care home;

(b) the outbreak of any infectious disease at the care home or involving children accommodated at the care home,

he will not be required to give separate notice of that event to the Commission under regulation 37 (notification of death, illness and other events) of these Regulations.

Fitness of workers

33. Regulation 19 shall have effect as if -

(a) in sub-paragraph (b) of paragraph (1) and sub-paragraph (b) of paragraph (4), for head (i) in each of those sub-paragraphs there were substituted the following head -

" (i) paragraphs 1 to 6 of Schedule 2 and in Schedule 6;";

(b) in sub-paragraph (d) of paragraph (5), for head (i) there were substituted the following head -

" (i) each of the matters specified in paragraphs 1 to 6 of Schedule 2 and in Schedule 6;";

(c) at the end of paragraph (5) there were added the following -

" and
(d) his qualifications, skills and experience are suitable for the purpose of working with children.".

Staff disciplinary procedure

34. The registered person shall operate a staff disciplinary procedure which, in particular -

(a) provides for the suspension of an employee of his where necessary in the interests of the safety or welfare of children accommodated in the care home; and

(b) provides that the failure on the part of an employee of his to report an incident of abuse, or suspected abuse of a child accommodated in the care home to an appropriate person is a ground on which disciplinary proceedings may be instituted.

Review of quality of care

35. Regulation 24 shall have effect as if -

(a) the system referred to in paragraph (1) of regulation 24 included monitoring at appropriate intervals the matters set out in Schedule 7;

(b) in paragraph (2) of regulation 24, after the words "any review conducted by him" there were added the words ", or any matters monitored";

(c) in paragraph (3) of regulation 24, for the words "and their representatives" there were substituted the words ", their representatives, the parents of the children accommodated at the care home and, in relation to those children, the placing authorities".

Offences

36. Regulation 43 shall have effect as if for paragraph (1) there were substituted the following paragraph -

" (1) A contravention or failure to comply with any of the following provisions shall be an offence -

(a) regulations 4, 5, 11, 12(1) to (4), 13(1) to (4) and (6) to (8), 14, 15, 16(1), (2)(a) to (j) and (l) to (n) and (3), 17 to 26 and 37 to 40, to the extent that those regulations have effect subject to Part VI of these Regulations;

(b) regulations 31 and 34; and

(c) the provisions referred to in paragraph (2) of regulation 32, to the extent that they apply to the registered person by virtue of that paragraph.".

PART VII

MISCELLANEOUS

Notification of death, illness and other events

37. - (1) The registered person shall give notice to the Commission without delay of the occurrence of -

(a) the death of any service user, including the circumstances of his death;

(b) the outbreak in the care home of any infectious disease which in the opinion of any registered medical practitioner attending persons in the care home is sufficiently serious to be so notified;

(c) any serious injury to a service user;

(d) serious illness of a service user at a care home at which nursing is not provided;

(e) any event in the care home which adversely affects the well-being or safety of any service user;

(f) any theft, burglary or accident in the care home;

(g) any allegation of misconduct by the registered person or any person who works at the care home.

(2) Any notification made in accordance with this regulation which is given orally shall be confirmed in writing.

Notice of absence

38. - (1) Where -

(a) the registered provider, if he is an individual; or

(b) the registered manager,

proposes to be absent from the care home for a continuous period of 28 days or more, the registered person shall give notice in writing to the Commission of the proposed absence.

(2) Except in the case of an emergency, the notice referred to in paragraph (1) above shall be given no later than one month before the proposed absence commences or within such shorter period as may be agreed with the Commission and the notice shall specify -

(a) the length or expected length of the absence;

(b) the reason for the absence;

(c) the arrangements which have been made for the running of the care home during that absence;

(d) the name, address and qualifications of the person who will be responsible for the care home during that absence; and

(e) in the case of the absence of the registered manager, the arrangements that have been, or are proposed to be, made for appointing another person to manage the care home during that absence, including the proposed date by which the appointment is to be made.

(3) Where the absence arises as a result of an emergency, the registered person shall give notice of the absence within one week of its occurrence specifying the matters mentioned in sub-paragraphs (a) to (e) of paragraph (2).

(4) Where -

(a) the registered provider, if he is an individual; or

(b) the registered manager,

has been absent from the care home for a continuous period of 28 days or more, and the Commission has not been given notice of the absence, the registered person shall without delay give notice in writing to the Commission of the absence, specifying the matters mentioned in sub-paragraphs (a) to (e) of paragraph (2).

(5) The registered person shall notify the Commission of the return to duty of the registered provider or (as the case may be) the registered manager not later than 7 days after the date of his return.

Notice of changes

39. The registered person shall give notice in writing to the Commission as soon as it is practicable to do so if any of the following events takes place or is proposed to take place -

(a) a person other than the registered person carries on or manages the care home;

(b) a person ceases to carry on or manage the care home;

(c) where the registered person is an individual, he changes his name;

(d) where the registered provider is a partnership, there is any change in the membership of the partnership;

(e) where the registered provider is an organisation -

(i) the name or address of the organisation is changed;

(ii) there is any change of director, manager, secretary or other similar officer of the organisation;

(iii) there is to be any change of responsible individual;

(f) where the registered provider is an individual, a trustee in bankruptcy is appointed;

(g) where the registered provider is a company or partnership, a receiver, manager, liquidator or provisional liquidator is appointed; or

(h) the premises of the care home are significantly altered or extended, or additional premises are acquired.

Notice of termination of accommodation

40. - (1) Subject to paragraph (2), the registered person shall not terminate the arrangements for the accommodation of a service user unless he has given reasonable notice of his intention to do so to -

(a) the service user;

(b) the person who appears to be the service user's next of kin; and

(c) where a local authority has made arrangements for the provision of accommodation, nursing or personal care to the service user at the care home, that authority.

(2) If it is impracticable for the registered person to comply with the requirement in paragraph (1) -

(a) he shall do so as soon as it is practicable to do so; and

(b) he shall provide to the Commission a statement as to the circumstances which made it impracticable for him to comply with the requirement.

Appointment of liquidators etc.

41. - (1) Any person to whom paragraph (2) applies must -

(a) forthwith notify the Commission of his appointment, indicating the reasons for it;

(b) appoint a manager to take full-time day to day charge of the care home in any case where there is no registered manager; and

(c) within 28 days of his appointment notify the Commission of his intentions regarding the future operation of the care home.

(2) This paragraph applies to any person appointed as -

(a) the receiver or manager of the property of a company or partnership which is a registered provider in respect of a care home;

(b) a liquidator or provisional liquidator of a company which is a registered provider of a care home; or

(c) the trustee in bankruptcy of a registered provider of a care home.

Death of registered person

42. - (1) If more than one person is registered in respect of a care home, and a registered person dies, the surviving registered person shall without delay notify the Commission of the death in writing.

(2) If only one person is registered in respect of a care home, and he dies, his personal representatives shall notify the Commission in writing -

(a) without delay of the death; and

(b) within 28 days of their intentions regarding the future running of the home.

(3) The personal representatives of the deceased registered provider may carry on the care home without being registered in respect of it -

(a) for a period not exceeding 28 days; and

(b) for any further period as may be determined in accordance with paragraph (4).

(4) The Commission may extend the period specified in paragraph (3)(a) by such further period, not exceeding one year, as the Commission shall determine, and shall notify any such determination to the personal representatives in writing.

(5) The personal representatives shall appoint a person to take full-time day to day charge of the home during any period in which, in accordance with paragraph (3), they carry on the care home without being registered in respect of it.

Offences

43. - (1) A contravention or failure to comply with any of the provisions of regulations 4, 5, 11, 12(1) to (4), 13(1) to (4) and (6) to (8), 14, 15, 16(1), (2)(a) to (j) and (1) to (n) and (3), 17 to 26 and 37 to 40, shall be an offence.

(2) The Commission shall not bring proceedings against a person in respect of any contravention or failure to comply with those regulations unless -

(a) subject to paragraph (4), he is a registered person;

(b) notice has been given to him in accordance with paragraph (3);

(c) the period specified in the notice, within which the registered person may make representations to the Commission, has expired; and

(d) in a case where, in accordance with paragraph (3)(b), the notice specifies any action that is to be taken within a specified period, the period has expired and the action has not been taken within that period.

(3) Where the Commission considers that the registered person has contravened or failed to comply with any of the provisions of the regulations mentioned in paragraph (1), it may serve a notice on the registered person specifying -

(a) in what respect in its opinion the registered person has contravened or is contravening any of the regulations, or has failed or is failing to comply with the requirements of any of the regulations;

(b) where it is practicable for the registered person to take action for the purpose of complying with any of those regulations, the action which, in the opinion of the Commission, the registered person should take for that purpose;

(c) the period, not exceeding three months, within which the registered person should take any action specified in accordance with sub-paragraph (b);

(d) the period, not exceeding one month, within which the registered person may make representations to the Commission about the notice.

(4) The Commission may bring proceedings against a person who was once, but no longer is, a registered person, in respect of a failure to comply with regulation 17 and for this purpose, references in paragraphs (2) and (3) to a registered person shall be taken to include such a

person.

Compliance with regulations

44. Where there is more than one registered person in respect of a care home, anything which is required under these regulations to be done by the registered person shall, if done by one of the registered persons, not be required to be done by any of the other registered persons.

Adult placements

45. - (1) For the purposes of this regulation and regulation 46, a registered provider is an adult placement carer in respect of a care home if -

(a) he is the registered provider in respect of, and manages, the care home;

(b) no person other than the registered provider manages the care home;

(c) the care home is, or forms part of -

(i) the registered provider's home; or

(ii) if the registered provider has more than one home, the home where he ordinarily resides;

(d) no more than three service users are accommodated in the care home;

(e) a placement agreement has been made in respect of each of the service users;

(f) each service user is over the age of 18.

(2) In this regulation, "placement agreement" means an agreement that -

(a) has been made between -

(i) the registered provider;

(ii) the service user;

(iii) the local authority or other body which manages a scheme ("adult placement scheme") under which it has arranged or proposes to arrange for the service user to be accommodated in a care home;

(b) makes provision for the following matters -

(i) the aims of the arrangements under which the service user is accommodated in the care home;

(ii) the room to be occupied by the service user;

(iii) the services to be provided to the service user;

(iv) the fees to be charged;

(v) the qualifications and experience of the registered provider;

(vi) the terms and conditions in respect of the accommodation and services to be provided;

(vii) services and assistance to be provided under the adult placement scheme under which the accommodation is or has been arranged.

Modification of regulations in respect of adult placement carers

46. - (1) The following provisions of this regulation shall apply where the registered provider is an adult placement carer in respect of a care home.

(2) Regulations 4, 8, 18, 19, 21, 24, 26 to 36 and 41 (statement of purpose; appointment of manager; staffing; fitness of workers; staff views as to conduct of care home; review of quality of care home; visits by registered provider; children; appointment of liquidators etc.) and Schedules 1 and 5 to 7 (information to be included in the statement of purpose; additional information to be included in the statement of purpose where children are accommodated; additional information and documents to be obtained in respect of persons working at a care home where children are accommodated; and matters to be monitored at a care home where children are accommodated) shall not apply.

(3) Regulation 5 (service user's guide) shall have effect as if sub-paragraph (a) of paragraph (1) of that regulation were omitted.

(4) Regulation 6 (review of statement of purpose and service user's guide) shall have effect as if in paragraph (a) of that regulation the words "the statement of purpose and" were omitted.

(5) Regulation 16 (facilities and services) shall have effect as if in sub-paragraph (j) of paragraph (2) of that regulation the words "after consultation with the environmental health authority" were omitted.

(6) Regulation 23 (fitness of premises) shall have effect as if sub-paragraphs (a), (f), (g), (h), (j), (k) and (n) of paragraph (2) and paragraphs (3) to (5) of that regulation were omitted.

(7) Regulation 25 (financial position) shall have effect as if -

(a) paragraph (1) of that regulation were omitted;

(b) in paragraph (2) of that regulation, sub-paragraphs (a) to (d) were omitted;

(c) paragraphs (3) and (4) of that regulation were omitted.

(8) Schedule 3 (records to be kept in a care home in respect of each service user) shall have effect as if sub-paragraph (j) of paragraph 3 of that Schedule were omitted.

(9) Schedule 4 (other records to be kept in a care home) shall have effect as if paragraphs 1, 3, 5, 6, 7 and 12 to 16 of that Schedule were omitted.

Signed by authority of the Secretary of State for Health

Jacqui Smith
Minister of State, Department of Health

11th December 2001

INFORMATION TO BE INCLUDED IN THE STATEMENT OF PURPOSE

1. The name and address of the registered provider and of any registered manager.

2. The relevant qualifications and experience of the registered provider and any registered manager.

3. The number, relevant qualifications and experience of the staff working at the care home.

4. The organisational structure of the care home.

5. The age-range and sex of the service users for whom it is intended that accommodation should be provided.

6. The range of needs that the care home is intended to meet.

7. Whether nursing is to be provided.

8. Any criteria used for admission to the care home, including the care home's policy and procedures (if any) for emergency admissions.

9. The arrangements for service users to engage in social activities, hobbies and leisure interests.

10. The arrangements made for consultation with service users about the operation of the care home.

11. The fire precautions and associated emergency procedures in the care home.

12. The arrangements made for service users to attend religious services of their choice.

13. The arrangements made for contact between service users and their relatives, friends and representatives.

14. The arrangements made for dealing with complaints.

15. The arrangements made for dealing with reviews of the service user's plan referred to in regulation 15(1).

16. The number and size of rooms in the care home.

17. Details of any specific therapeutic techniques used in the care home and arrangements made for their supervision.

18. The arrangements made for respecting the privacy and dignity of service users.

INFORMATION AND DOCUMENTS IN RESPECT OF PERSONS CARRYING ON, MANAGING OR WORKING AT A CARE HOME

1. Proof of the person's identity, including a recent photograph.

2. The person's birth certificate.

3. The person's current passport (if any).

4. Documentary evidence of any relevant qualifications of the person.

5. Two written references relating to the person.

6. Evidence that the person is physically and mentally fit for the purposes of the work which he is to perform at the care home or, where it is impracticable for the person to obtain such evidence, a declaration signed by the person that he is so fit.

7. Either -

(a) where the certificate is required for a purpose relating to section 115(5)(ea) of the Police Act 1997 (registration under Part II of the Care Standards Act 2000)[11], or the position falls within section 115(3) or (4) of that Act[12], an enhanced criminal record certificate issued under section 115 of that Act; or

(b) in any other case, a criminal record certificate issued under section 113 of that Act,

including, where applicable, the matters specified in section 113(3A) and 115(6A) of that Act and the following provisions once they are in force, namely section 113(3C)(a) and (b) and section 115(6B)(a) and (b) of that Act[13].

SCHEDULE 3

Regulation 17(1)(a)

RECORDS TO BE KEPT IN A CARE HOME IN RESPECT OF EACH SERVICE USER

1. The following documents in respect of each service user -

(a) the assessment referred to in regulation 14(1);

(b) the service user's plan referred to in regulation 15(1).

2. A photograph of the service user.

3. A record of the following matters in respect of each service user -

(a) the name, address, date of birth and marital status of each service user;

(b) the name, address and telephone number of the service user's next of kin or of any person authorised to act on his behalf;

(c) the name, address and telephone number of the service user's general practitioner and of any officer of a local social services authority whose duty it is to supervise the welfare of the service user;

(d) the date on which the service user entered the care home;

(e) the date on which the service user left the care home;

(f) if the service user is transferred to another care home or to a hospital, the name of the care home or hospital and the date on which the service user is transferred;

(g) if the service user died at the care home, the date, time and cause of death;

(h) the name and address of any authority, organisation or other body, which arranged the service user's admission to the care home;

(i) a record of all medicines kept in the care home for the service user, and the date on which they were administered to the service user;

(j) a record of any accident affecting the service user in the care home and of any other incident in the care home which is detrimental to the health or welfare of the service user, which record shall include the nature, date and time of the accident or incident, whether medical treatment was required and the name of the persons who were respectively in charge of the care home and supervising the service user;

(k) a record of any nursing provided to the service user, including a record of his condition and any treatment or surgical intervention;

(l) details of any specialist communications needs of the service user and methods of communication that may be appropriate to the service user;

(m) details of any plan relating to the service user in respect of medication, nursing, specialist health care or nutrition;

(n) a record of incidence of pressure sores and of treatment provided to the service user;

(o) a record of falls and of treatment provided to the service user;

(p) a record of any physical restraint used on the service user;

(q) a record of any limitations agreed with the service user as to the service user's freedom of choice, liberty of movement and power to make decisions.

4. A copy of correspondence relating to each service user.

OTHER RECORDS TO BE KEPT IN A CARE HOME

1. A copy of the statement of purpose.

2. A copy of the service user's guide.

3. A record of all accounts kept in the care home.

4. A copy of all inspection reports.

5. A copy of any report made under regulation 26(4)(c).

6. A record of all persons employed at the care home, including in respect of each person so employed -

(a) his full name, address, date of birth, qualifications and experience;

(b) a copy of his birth certificate and passport;

(c) a copy of each reference obtained in respect of him;

(d) the dates on which he commences and ceases to be so employed;

(e) the position he holds at the care home, the work that he performs and the number of hours for which he is employed each week;

(f) correspondence, reports, records of disciplinary action and any other records in relation to his employment.

7. A copy of the duty roster of persons working at the care home, and a record of whether the roster was actually worked.

8. A record of the care home's charges to service users, including any extra amounts payable for additional services not covered by those charges, and the amounts paid by or in respect of each service user.

9. A record of all money or other valuables deposited by a service user for safekeeping or received on the service user's behalf, which -

(a) shall state the date on which the money or valuables were deposited or received, the date on which any money or valuables were returned to a service user or used, at the request of the service user, on his behalf and, where applicable, the purpose for which the money or valuables were used; and

(b) shall include the written acknowledgement of the return of the money or valuables.

10. A record of furniture brought by a service user into the room occupied by him.

11. A record of all complaints made by service users or representatives or relatives of service users or by persons working at the care home about the operation of the care home, and the action taken by the registered person in respect of any such complaint.

12. A record of any of the following events that occur in the care home -

(a) any accident;

(b) any incident which is detrimental to the health or welfare of a service user, including the outbreak of infectious disease in the care home;

(c) any injury or illness;

(d) any fire;

(e) except where a record to which paragraph 14 refers is to be made, any occasion on which the fire alarm equipment is operated;

(f) any theft or burglary.

13. Records of the food provided for service users in sufficient detail to enable any person inspecting the record to determine whether the diet is satisfactory, in relation to nutrition and otherwise, and of any special diets prepared for individual service users.

14. A record of every fire practice, drill or test of fire equipment (including fire alarm equipment) conducted in the care home and of any action taken to remedy defects in the fire equipment.

15. A statement of the procedure to be followed in the event of a fire, or where a fire alarm is given.

16. A statement of the procedure to be followed in the event of accidents or in the event of a service user becoming missing.

17. A record of all visitors to the care home, including the names of visitors.

SCHEDULE 5

ADDITIONAL INFORMATION TO BE INCLUDED IN THE STATEMENT OF PURPOSE
WHERE CHILDREN ARE ACCOMMODATED

1. The following details about the children for whom it is intended that accommodation should be provided -

(a) their age-range;

(b) their sex;

(c) the number of children;

(d) whether they are disabled, have special needs or any other special characteristics; and

(e) the range of needs that the care home is intended to meet.

2. Any criteria used for admission to the care home, including the care home's policy and procedures for emergency admissions, if applicable.

3. If the care home provides or is intended to provide accommodation for more than six children, a description of the positive outcomes intended for children in a care home of such a size, and of the care home's strategy for counteracting any adverse effects arising from its size, on the children accommodated there.

4. A description of the care home's underlying ethos and philosophy, and where this is based on any theoretical or therapeutic model, a description of that model.

5. The facilities and services to be provided or made available, within and outside the care home, for the children accommodated there.

6. The arrangements made to protect and promote the health of the children accommodated there.

7. The arrangements for the promotion of the education of the children accommodated there, including the facilities for private study.

8. The arrangements to promote children's participation in hobbies and recreational, sporting and cultural activities.

9. The arrangements made for consultation with the children accommodated there about the operation of the care home.

10. The policy on behaviour management and the use of restraint in the care home, including in particular the methods of control and discipline and the disciplinary measures which may be used, the circumstances in which any such measures will be used and who will be permitted to use and authorise them.

11. The arrangements for child protection and to counter bullying.

12. The fire precautions and associated emergency procedures in the care home.

13. The arrangements made for the children's religious instruction and observance.

14. The arrangements made for contact between a child accommodated there and his parents, relatives and friends.

15. The procedure for dealing with any unauthorised absence of a child from the care home.

16. The arrangements for dealing with complaints.

17. The arrangements for dealing with reviews of the placement plans of children accommodated there.

18. The type of accommodation and sleeping arrangements provided, and, where applicable, how children are to be grouped, and in what circumstances they are to share bedrooms.

19. Details of any specific therapeutic techniques used in the care home and arrangements for their supervision.

20. A description of the care home's policy on anti-discriminatory practice in relation to children and children's rights.

SCHEDULE 6

Regulations 19 and 33(b)

ADDITIONAL INFORMATION AND DOCUMENTS TO BE OBTAINED IN RESPECT OF PERSONS WORKING AT A CARE HOME WHERE CHILDREN ARE ACCOMMODATED

1. Two written references, including a reference from the last employer.

2. Where a person has previously worked in a position whose duties involved work with children or vulnerable adults, so far as reasonably practicable, verification of the reason why the employment or position ended.

3. A full employment history, together with a satisfactory written explanation of any gaps in employment.

SCHEDULE 7

Regulations 24 and 35(a)

MATTERS TO BE MONITORED AT A CARE HOME WHERE CHILDREN ARE ACCOMMODATED

1. Compliance with any plan for the care of the child prepared by the placing authority and the placement plan of each child accommodated in the care home.

2. The deposit and issue of money and other valuables handed in for safekeeping.

3. Daily menus.

4. All accidents and injuries sustained in the care home or by children accommodated there.

5. Any illnesses of children accommodated in the care home.

6. Complaints in relation to children accommodated in the care home and their outcomes.

7. Any allegations or suspicions of abuse in respect of children accommodated in the care home and the outcome of any investigation.

8. Staff recruitment records and conduct of required checks for new workers in the care home.

9. Visitors to the care home and to children in the care home.

10. Notifications of the events listed in Schedule 5 to the Children's Homes Regulations 2001.

11. Any unauthorised absence from the care home of a child accommodated there.

12. The use of disciplinary measures in respect of children accommodated in the care home.

13. The use of physical restraint in respect of children accommodated in the care home.

EXPLANATORY NOTE

(This note is not part of the Regulations)

These Regulations are made under the Care Standards Act 2000 ("the Act") and apply to England only. Part I of the Act establishes, in relation to England, the National Care Standards Commission ("the Commission") and Part II provides for the registration and inspection of establishments and agencies, including care homes, by the Commission. It also provides powers for regulations governing the conduct of establishments and agencies. The majority of Parts I and II of the Act (in so far as not already in force) will be brought into force on 1 April 2002.

These new arrangements replace the regulatory system provided for in relation to residential care homes and nursing homes by the Registered Homes Act 1984.

Regulation 3 excludes from the definition of a care home under section 3 of the Act certain NHS hospitals and establishments providing nursing, universities, schools and certain further education institutions.

Under regulations 4 and 5, each home must have a statement of purpose consisting of the matters set out in Schedule 1, and supply a guide to the home to each service user.

Regulations 7 to 10 make provision about the fitness of the persons carrying on and managing the home, and require satisfactory information to be available in relation to certain specified matters. Where an organisation carries on the home, it must nominate a responsible individual in respect of whom this information must be available (regulation 7). Regulation 8 prescribes the circumstances where a manager must be appointed for the home, and regulation 10 imposes general requirements in relation to the proper conduct of the home, and the need for appropriate training.

Part III makes provision about the conduct of care homes, in particular as to health and welfare of service users, and as to the facilities and services that are to be provided. Provision is also made about record keeping, the staffing of homes, the fitness of workers, and about complaints.

Part IV makes provision about the suitability of premises and fire precautions to be taken. Part V deals with the management of care homes. Regulation 24 requires the registered person to establish a system for reviewing and improving the quality of care provided by the home. Regulation 25 imposes requirements relating to the home's financial position. Regulation 26 requires the registered provider to visit the home as prescribed. Part VI makes special provision which applies where children are accommodated at the home.

Part VII deals with miscellaneous matters including the giving of notices to the Commission. Regulation 43 provides for offences. A breach of the regulations specified in regulation 43 may found an offence on the part of the registered person. However, no prosecution may be brought unless the Commission has first given the registered person a notice which sets out in what respect it is alleged he is not complying with a regulation, and what action the Commission considers it is necessary for him to take in order to comply. The notice must specify a time period for compliance, not exceeding three months.

Notes:

[1] 2000 c. 14. The powers are exercisable by the appropriate Minister, who is defined in section 121(1), in relation to England, Scotland and Northern Ireland, as the Secretary of State. *See* section 121(1) for the definitions of "prescribed" and "regulations".back

[2] *See* section 22(9) of the Care Standards Act 2000 for the requirement to consult.back

[3] 10 & 11 Geo.6 c. 41.back

[4] 1977 c. 49.back

[5] 1997 c. 46.back

[6] 1999 c. 8.back

[7] 1977 c. 49.back

[8] *See* section 5 of the National Health Service and Community Care Act 1990 (c. 19) as amended by paragraph 69 of Schedule 1 to the Health Authorities Act 1995 (c. 17) and section 13(1) of the Health Act 1999 (c. 8).back

[9] 1992 c. 13.back

[10] S.I. 2001/3967.back

[11] 1997 c. 50. Section 115(5)(ea) was inserted by the Care Standards Act 2000, section 104, on a date to be appointed. Sections 113 and 115, as amended, have not yet been brought into force.back

[12] A position is within section 115(3) if it involves regularly caring for, training, supervising or being in sole charge of persons aged under 18. A position is within section 115(4) if it is of a kind specified in regulations and involves regularly caring for, training, supervising or being in sole charge of persons aged 18 or over.back

[13] Section 113(3A) and 115(6A) are added to the Police Act 1997 by section 8 of the Protection of Children Act 1999 (c. 14), and amended by sections 104 and 116 of, and paragraph 25 of Schedule 4 to, the Care Standards Act 2000. Sections 113(3C) and 115(6B) are added to the Police Act 1997 by section 90 of the Care Standards Act 2000 on a date to be appointed.back

[14] 1974 c. 53.back

[15] S.I. 1975/1023. Relevant amending instruments are S.I. 1986/1249, 1986/2268, 2001/1192.back

ISBN 0 11 039231 0